THIS VERY TREE

BY THE SAME AUTHOR
Written in Sand : Freedom's Farm
At Midnight on the 31st of March

THIS

VERY

TREE

Josephine Young Case

HOUGHTON MIFFLIN COMPANY
BOSTON

1969

FRONTISPIECE
BY MEREDITH K. WILDES

First Printing   w

Library of Congress Catalog Card Number 69–19566
Printed in the United States of America

FOR THE CHILDREN IN
THE BIG HOUSE

I see now that the College which we knew, so short a time ago, is already one with the infant Academy of a hundred and fifty years past. Changes indeed we saw, in twenty years on campus, and foresaw others, as we watched the water changing in the river. But the speed of the current has increased so greatly in the last few years that we are strangers where once we drew out our canoes.

Yet an hour's assistance at the spectacle of the College's past, new acts and changing scenes, proves the long continuity on the same stage. No one, in this country and this day, expects anything to remain the same: hence I celebrate the identity of our College, the variety of her history, and the maintenance over so long a time of her ethos.

•

THIS VERY TREE

I

We went up the hill, the dogs and I, far up beyond the College, to the edge of the woods where the old hemlock stands looking down on the slate roofs, even down upon the gilded spire of the chapel. It is not so tall a tree, as old trees go, but it is far taller than its companions, and its trunk is immense. To touch the bark is to feel decades and centuries living beneath the hand. For it was here long before the College, it was here when there were only Indians to see it and even then its feathered top was a marker for the trail that ran from crest to crest of the long hills. Indeed it was here, so slow do hemlocks grow, when the grounding of English keels upon the eastern shore sent through all the continent the first faint shock.

Under this tree, they said, Isaac Garrow, the first owner of this hill, met Azel Champion when he came from New England to the new little settlement in New York State to be its first minister. And it was those two, ten years later, who founded the College. With my hand upon the trunk I stood under the feathery branches where the hill-wind spoke, and thought of them, and looked down upon the College and the village and the wide valley beyond where an oxbow of the Canowenda glimmered among the willows.

Because it was September and the air just honing an edge we ran down across the fields, the dogs racing with flags flying, till the College buildings closed around us. The oldest, Champion Hall, which was once all the College there was, already wore a crimson creeper on its worn stone. I looked at the small-paned windows where a face moved behind the dark uneven glass: was it Azel himself? He built this building, partly with his own hands, he built the idea of the College too and shaped them both in nowhere from nothing; and both are here today. Immortal, I thought, with a shiver at the back of the neck, there is an immortal presence here, that dwells upon this hill. It is a presence made up of persons and ideas, of hundreds of teachers, thousands of young men, who have paused for a few years of their lives in these buildings, under these trees: a hundred and fifty years of teaching and learning on this spot, to which Azel Champion gave a local habitation and a name.

•

That was the year, in the early fifties, I decided to *do* something. The difficult years of the war were behind us and the College was once more on an even keel. Indeed, it was full of the vigor and hope that ran through all the nation in those expanding times. For me, the classical point in a woman's life had been reached: the youngest child was now in school all day. The dogs, cats and I were chasing each other around the enormous President's House, and I wanted a new course, a new project, a demanding job.

Mathias gave me a very husbandly look when, that evening, I told him this. All he said was, "Isn't being the President's wife enough for you?"

It should have been, of course. There were plenty of jobs, meetings, entertaining, and it took plenty of time to keep the wonderful rickety old house always in order — not to mention the children.

Still, he was sympathetic. "What do you *want* to do?"

"I don't know."

"Well, what are you interested in?"

"Too many things."

"But mainly?"

I thought of the afternoon's walk. "Mainly I'm interested in the College. This is my life, your life, our lives for years past, years to come."

The President absentmindedly made another martini. "But you are working with the College all the time. You see faculty and students, you are in touch with almost everything. What more do you want?"

I was dreaming over the ice-cold glass. "The past, I think. What made it the way it is: the history of the beginning, the middle, and the now, which is so different, yet probably so much the same." I looked up at him. "I could write something about it."

He shook his head. "There's a History of the College under way. Satterwell was working on it."

"I know. But he died."

"Then the job was given to Amos Whitefield. I suppose he's working on it now."

I had never known Professor Whitefield very well. He was Professor Emeritus of Classics, a widower, and not one to come to my faculty teas: a little old white-haired man who lived in a little old white house opposite the campus. I used to meet him, wiry, active, bareheaded, on walks; indeed we seemed to be the only people in the College who went walking for pleasure. He would bow to me, and I knew if he ever wore a hat he would have swept it off. But we were both too shy to talk.

Matt said, "I think Satterwell did a lot of research before he popped off. But there's probably more to do, not to mention typing and editing. Why don't you help Dr. Whitefield with the History, if he wants you to?"

"Why would he want some female barging in — the President's wife at that? He might think he had to say yes when he hated the idea."

"He wouldn't. Ask him anyway, if you want to do it. From what I know of Amos he would be fun to work with."

II

It was not until October that I went down the hill to ask him, for September is always a frantically busy month. First, the campus is empty, expectant, the dormitories and fraternity houses vacant, the roads untraveled; the Dean's Office, the Registrar's Office readying their machinery, the dining halls beginning to receive the great lava-flow of food, the garbage cans scrubbed and empty; the faculty, schedules in hand, waiting with the superficial cynicism and secret excitement with which they greet each new year.

Then suddenly they were there, hundreds and hundreds of them, from nowhere, from everywhere they appeared; with the infinite mysterious mobility of young men they were not there one moment and there in crowds the next, almost all of them on time, almost all of them in one piece.

Then, as always, the weather turned warm, so that as I went down the hill I saw them lying on the lawns in shorts, showing off their summer tan. They were surrounded by books, the new books, the syllabi, the schedules of the new year; but they were not opening them. They were lying on their backs, looking at the first turning leaves and talking of summer. Summer had already passed into legend, with its parties and jobs and girls all more glamorous or more terrible than life. They looked like creatures of legend themselves, half-naked in the sun, lotus-eaters out of a classical past. How will they do, I thought, in classroom and library and laboratory? What will develop under those brown or black or golden thatches, through the endless ticking over of the brain cells, what will develop that will change them, and the world?

At Convocation I had watched them, as the faculty came in resplendent in black and colored silks, as the President spoke, as the Chaplain prayed "that knowledge may be increased among us and all good learning flourish and abound. Bless all who teach and all who learn —" They were very quiet, as though they felt the presence around them; I knew that they were touched because they were so noisy when they went out of the chapel into the sunshine.

Then of course we had Freshman Reception, when over our vacation faces we put on once more the masks of the President and his wife. We laughed, we chatted, we shook their hands; but it is always a serious occasion, a rite, an acceptance of the neophyte into the sacred grove. Their palms are wet, their voices untrustworthy, their eyes averted. And we — we look eagerly at them, seeking at first glance to know them, to see into their hearts. They think we are the College; but we know it is they.

Now as I went down the hill hop skip and jump I saw that fall was fully here. At the top of the long main street that is our village, sloping down to the river at its foot, the maples were scarlet around the Civil War cannon in the little triangle park where Main and Maple come together. The oaks were barely turning along the edges of the lawns, but the squirrels were busy. What is your history,

I asked, are you descendants of First Founding Squirrels? Were you here already, like our tree, when we came to build the College?

I slowed down as I neared Dr. Whitefield's house, for I was a little frightened at my errand. It was because I did not know him well, and felt for him, as I do for some of the older faculty, awe. I had seen him the day before, downtown, talking with Nap Vincent in front of Nap's paper store. He had an empty string bag in his hand and, like me, was on his way to market. Nap is a friend of all the students and almost all the faculty; he has kept his eye on everything along Main Street for ten generations of students, and they say the bull sessions among the White Owl cigars and the girly magazines are as good as any seminar on the hill.

While I was in the market Dr. Whitefield came in, and I saw him, at a distance, among the sardines. Like a white-headed heron, I thought, he looks carefully till he sees the fish he wants, then seizes it quickly and puts it in the string bag: lonely lonely lonely heron.

When I stood on the porch beneath the Greek Revival columns there was no answer to my knock, but I caught sight through the lilac hedge of his white head in the garden. His hair was like snow, thick and very short.

He was planting tulip bulbs, and obviously felt that he should stop and receive me more formally in the house. But I persuaded him to continue, and handed him the bulbs as he made neat little holes in his perfect garden soil.

It was warm there, sheltered from the wind, and the sun was beginning to come unshadowed to the grass; the leaves were falling slowly as we worked.

He finished with the "Lady of Haarlem" and I handed him the first of the "Spirits of the Night."

"Do you know these?" he asked. "They are magnificent. I think they will look like the great Queen herself as she appeared before Solomon in purple glinting with gold. I shall put them here, behind the primroses, who will serve as handmaidens in yellow and bronze."

He held the bulb, dry, flaking, as though he felt the Queen move within it. "I have never had this variety in my garden before." Then he said like a child, "They are very expensive. And I bought twenty-five!" And as he made the first royal hole he muttered, "It was the fee for the History, of course, that is putting them here."

So I talked to him about the History, and asked how it was coming, and said if I could be of any help I would be happy to volunteer, because of my great interest in the College's past. He got up and brushed his knees carefully, then looked at me where I sat on the great stone with a sudden and wholly charming smile. "I would be delighted to have your assistance," he said formally.

We looked over the material in the study as the sun dropped from the garden. There were books, old catalogs, pamphlets dog-eared and dusty, and a file box of cards which Professor Satterwell had put together.

"A woodchuck," said Dr. Whitefield suddenly and mysteriously. Then he gave the little chuckling cough which already I knew to be characteristic. "Satterwell I mean. He looked like a woodchuck in his study; his papers and books made a burrow around him. I think he liked the physical presence of books more than reading them; they were good to build burrows with." He sighed. "When I went to fetch this stuff after the woodchuck was dug in for good Mrs. Satterwell had the place all cleaned up."

The cards were organized chronologically, a section for each decade, a card or two for each year. Dr. Whitefield snapped the box shut with his beautiful hands with the garden dirt deep under the nails. "I don't mean to do it that way at all," he said.

The low sun made sparks in his eyes and he spoke like the Delphic oracle. "Everything that has passed in this College exists here now, everything that is to be is with the past and with us." He looked down at the piles of papers on the old desk. "I will be like Schliemann at Troy. I will begin at the top and dig down. I will uncover it layer by layer, seeking city beneath city. I will excavate and reconstruct many Colleges, and thus I will show there is but one."

III

The next time I went by Dr. Whitefield's house it was the Saturday of Homecoming, and I glimpsed his white crest in a ring of alumni on his front porch. Of course, I thought, of course they come back to see him; he must have been the kind of teacher who is never forgotten. But I was surprised to see Tuckerman Butterweck '17 leaning eagerly forward to catch a word; no classical scholar he, surely. He was purported to be our richest alumnus and Matt, I knew, had his eye on him for money for the new library we needed so badly.

The band came by on its way to the field, the brass flashing under the golden trees. Dr. Whitefield waved to them with the curious little lift of the hand, like an oriental gesture, that already I knew well. Then he pulled on his old shaggy brown overcoat and moved off after them with his gang of "boys." I knew that we would win if his enthusiasm was the deciding factor.

I had my own gang to cope with, for Homecoming fills the President's House for forty-eight hours of food, drink and lodging. The children are pushed into service, the dogs are exiled, the house is full of noise and movement and the smell of good food. All went well that weekend, however: the alumni found the campus just as they dreamed of it — the elms yellow, the maples crimson and vermilion and gold, the hawthorn glittering with bright berries above the emerald grass, the woodbine brilliant on the gray stone buildings. My heart warmed even to their clichés: Sure is great to be back, the old place looks great, you know it means a lot to me. I understand that what they want to say and cannot is: We deeply cherish this place, these lawns, these trees, these very stones, because of what went on here, without and within. With this ground we are more nearly one than elsewhere, it is forever part of us, from mornings when the first warmth of spring touched the snowbanks, from nights when the moon glittered on the river, from October days like this one: for here, then, voices spoke to us, from books, from men, from the trees and stones themselves, perhaps once only, or again.

When they were gone I planned another session on the History. And somehow, between a luncheon for six trumped up at the last moment because Matt had a sudden and secret crisis to discuss with a faculty committee, and the tea for new faculty wives at the Dean's house, I found two hours to spend with Dr. Whitefield. I walked down across the lawns in the wild autumn wind, scuffling in the leaves and thinking how, on the first days of bare trees, it is as though a great curtain had been rolled back and all the sky and sun and stars are extended newly for us in all their magnificence.

When I came into the study, for he had told me to walk in without knocking, he looked up from a Greek text. "My translation of Hesiod," he said, as though it were a child or a beloved pet. I had heard that he had been working on the definitive American translation of *The Works and Days* for the past forty years, and that — so ran faculty gossip — it was nowhere near done yet.

"May I read you this?" he asked. "It is pertinent to our history of the College." I liked the "our."

"It is about the word *ethos* which Hesiod uses in several passages, sometimes in the sense of 'character' or 'disposition'; or here, where he speaks of marrying a young wife so you can teach her good 'habits' — the same word. It means 'habits' in a larger sense too —" I could see he was well started for a gallop on his hobby, yet I thought how good a teacher he must have been, with his blue eyes bright with excitement at a word — "it means 'the customs of men.'" He turned to the big dictionary at his elbow. "Here it is. First it meant 'an accustomed place,' and in the plural 'seats, haunts, abodes, first of beasts, afterward of men.' Also, and this is a natural extension of the feeling of 'abode,' it means as I said, 'custom, usage, habit,' and hence, finally, 'disposition, temper, character.'" He shut the book with a soft thud and looked at me. Behind him the fall sunshine was bright in the window and I could see the smoke-colored stone of the old library behind the tracery of trees. "*Ethos* — that's what I want to get into this history, the ethos of the College: 'haunts, abodes, first of beasts but afterward of men.' Think of early days upon these hills before the white men came: then 'custom, usage, habit,' and then 'disposition, temper, character' — why, it's the history of the College in a word."

We turned to the piles of catalogs and pamphlets, old programs and syllabi, the detritus thrown up by the ethos. I began to sort, and he started to look through those of fifty and sixty years ago, when he himself was a student. There were smiles and mutterings, and at last he swung round his old-fashioned swivel chair and stared out of the window at the library, which, when he came, was the newest and most magnificent building on the campus. "It is impossible to live in the present," he said to himself more than to me, "without knowing the story of the past. But how can we know it, beyond our own span, and how can we write it so tomorrow will understand?"

As I left, when my time was up, and fought my way through the wind to the Dean's house, I felt the deep discouragement inevitable to and probably necessary for the beginning of a big job. Will there ever be time? Will we ever get down to the writing?

IV

Indeed the rest of October was a total loss as far as the History was concerned. I was immersed, drowned in duties. The first meeting of the club for the women of the College came sooner than I expected; it always does. The children and Butch were put to setting up seventy-five folding chairs for posteriors of all shapes and sizes. This was a job they all loved because it was active, noisy, and the results in well-ordered rows were satisfying.

Butch was that year's handyman. Each year the Dean of Students sends me a boy who needs money to do the extra chores. I have had a varied array, and this one did not impress me when he turned up trembling at the back door. An honor student from a small rural high school, he was a farm boy profiting by a scholarship given by an alumnus for a boy from his county. He was small, square, and blocky like his name, Blochmann. I asked his first name.

"Butch," he said.

"Not really," I said.

He shifted his feet. "It's Augustine." He pronounced in the German manner.

"Very well, Butch," I said, "we'll start washing the French windows where the dogs have put their muddy paws all over the glass."

We got on well, though he was so shy it hurt him to talk to me. I don't think he had ever been away from home before. But with the children he was wholly at home, and it was hard to tell who was the older as the metal chairs banged and clashed. "No," ordered my twelve-year-old, "that's too close, Butch. Mrs. Faxton could *never* get through there."

Next came the calling on new faculty wives, which must be done before too many weeks of the new academic year pass by. I drove myself to it, for I dread walking up to the door of a stranger; how bold to knock and expect to be taken in. And I knew that the inhabitants were often more surprised than pleased to see me on the doorstep.

Little Mrs. Jaffe had been lying down, I think, for when she came to the door one cheek was red and her eyes heavy-lidded. But it gave her a soft sleepy charm, like a child taken up from a nap, and I found myself speaking slowly and gently as to a child. For a moment she did not know who I was, but she quickly recovered and invited me in very nicely, and offered tea, which I refused. Whether it was sleepiness or shyness she did not talk easily — or perhaps she did not care to talk. Jaffe is a new instructor in the Romance Languages Department, coming from a big city university, and there was in her voice a faint trace of accent that indicated early years abroad. I asked her how she liked the College and the place.

"It is beautiful," she said hesitantly.

"But you miss the city?"

"Yes. Life," she hesitated, "is here so — how shall I say it? — so *shallow*, compared with the city."

I thought of the deep rich-woven life which is mine in this place. But I did not argue. I suggested several things that she could do; but she confessed she is pregnant and does not feel very well. This was their first child; they had been married three years, but felt they could afford a child with the appointment here. So we talked about having babies and some warmth came into her voice and face. I promised to send some books, and to ask some of my younger friends to come in. But as I went away I felt dissatisfied, and unequal to all I wanted to do.

When I finally had an afternoon for the History, Dr. Whitefield told me that Jack Ross in the Public Relations Office had asked him to provide, from the History, the text of a brochure for general information and fund-raising.

Dr. Whitefield quoted Jack with a little quirk at the side of his mouth. " 'Just a brief thing,' Jack said, 'concise but vivid, to tell the story of the wonderful background of the College — something dignified but arresting.' "

We both laughed, then he was off on a gallop again.

"What a curious word is 'brochure.' Do you know its history? It is the same stem as 'brooch' of course, and from that meaning of 'pin' or 'needle,' came the sense of 'a few pages sewed together.' And on the other hand it is the same as 'broach.' How delightful it is that one can Broach a campaign with a Brochure."

Finally I got him back to the subject. For I know that when Jack Ross wants something he does not mean the month after next or even the week. But Dr. Whitefield was still fussing.

"Ross said the history of the College is so unique, an incorrect phrase and a wrong idea. Of course it isn't unique; it's remarkably like the history of Union, or Hamilton, or Colgate, or Saint Lawrence. All our New York State colleges have much in common in their history, as the New England ones do. And yet, of course," he smiled at me as though only we two were in the secret, "there are characteristics which are typically ours: this setting, our special and traditional excellence in the liberal arts, some of the aspects of our history. And Ross did have one good idea: the continuity of the College — just what you and I have felt so strongly in working over our material — a continuity limitless in time but confined in space. It will be mostly pictures, of course, the brochure, but we must try to tell what even pictures cannot show — something of great men and great ideas."

He fell into a reverie. "How shall we begin?" I said with my pencil ready. He leaned back in his great chair and put his fingertips together as we used to do when we were playing "Here's the church and here's the steeple."

"A college is a country," he began . . .

~ II

November is pewter-colored on our hills; a pewter sky over the few dull clinging leaves, the grass turning brown, the far woods slate-blue. That year it was windless too, everything was still, as though we were living in an eye between the end and the beginning. It was a fifth season which the calendar did not show, a season of nothing.

Oppressed by the weather and the burden of things to do — meetings every day and Christmas coming — I gave my over-crowded desk a glance and decided to leave it all undone. I flung on my coat and banged out of the house and went to the library to look up some things for Amos. He had asked me to call him Amos and I was as proud as though he had made me his squire.

Our library was very old, ramshackle and falling apart, dark and crowded; but I loved its dusty musty smell and the sense of being shut away in a fortress. That day I slipped away into the stacks on the upper floor. There were only a few students there, with their heads or their feet on the little study tables. The radiators wheezed

softly like old professors and the air was warm with the
smell of books and boys.

I found on the History of Education shelves a few vol-
umes of autobiography and memoirs by alumni of the College. I sat down on the floor between the stacks to read a
description of life here in the latter part of the last century.

*We had to wear high boots because the campus was
mud much of the year. There were no sidewalks. I had
one good suit which I wore to dances; it was dark blue,
with a yellow linen vest, double-breasted. We always
wore gloves to dances too, and there was no drinking
then. But the fellows did plenty of drinking at other
times, usually on Fridays. I remember one Friday night
we got Prof. Wilmets' cow up into the lab. on the second floor of the science building, milked her dry, and left
her for him to find in the morning.*

*The faculty taught us everything, page by page, from
their own text-books. I never went into the Library
though when they built the new one my freshman year*
[that's this one, I thought] *I went inside to see what it
was like. But the professors knew everything, not only in
their own fields but in all, and tried to teach it all to us.
It was as though we took courses in the professors, not
the subjects. And they were interested in each one of us,
and cared about us. We all lived together like a family.*

Hm, I thought, I wonder if he was typical of the student of
that day; he sounds like Butch. A student had come into
my row, looking I am sure for something else. Do you feel

you are part of a family? I asked him silently. I do not think he would have said yes.

I pulled out another volume, by a member of the Class of 1895; I knew his name, for he had gone on to fame and fortune. He too had been a boy from a farm. I thought of Amos as I read the first sentence.

Coming to college was like landing in a foreign country. You had to learn the language and the customs, and to resemble the natives as quickly as possible. It was a small place, all by itself, self-centered and resistant to new ideas. But in some ways it was very much like the rest of the United States, — active, idealistic, and strongly competitive.

I went on along the shelf, taking some notes here and there. Amos knows this already, I thought, but I don't. We were working, following the excavation-of-Troy plan, on the period when he had been a student, and the decade just before.

"Yes," he said, when I reported to him that afternoon, "I knew both those men, and what they say is true, at least for them. But even in so small a college as this was then, there were many different experiences. Now mine —" he leaned back in his chair, the old leather creaking, and smiled at me. "Let me tell you how I felt when I came to college as a freshman." He reached for a book on a shelf at hand.

"Do you remember those old-fashioned romances — perhaps you are too young ever to have read them —

which always seemed to begin with the lonely traveler surmounting the final hill at dusk?" He handed me the book. It was a novel published in 1884, with a name in fine writing on the flyleaf: *Rose Freemantle Her Book 1893.* "Read the first paragraph," said Amos.

The stranger halted his horse and sat for a moment looking at the valley before him. Lights showed already from a window here and there in the town, and smoke curled from the chimneys. It was a peaceful scene, but in the heart of the traveller lay hope mingled with anxiety. What fortune awaited him in this place he had striven so long to reach?

The old professor smiled at me. "That was how I came to the College. Oh it wasn't just like that, of course. I came not on horseback but in my father's buggy, with my little trunk on behind and a cheesebox full of food on the seat beside me. It wasn't even the first time I had come here; we used to drive over sometimes from the farm to trade. But that evening, as I came over the hill — you know where they have recently cut back the bank on the east road? It used to curve very sharply there so that you suddenly came upon the valley and the College — I turned the corner just at sunset, and it seemed as though for the first time. I checked the horse. I remember his snatching at the leaves on the bank as I stared at the church steeples and on the slope of the far hill the three buildings that were the College. I sat there behind old gray Jacko and looked down upon my future, and felt indeed like that mysterious traveler who came late and anxious to his long-sought goal."

I said nothing, watching him, thinking about how he must have looked at that moment: thin, eager, his blue eyes alight. He chuckled a little and went on. "Of course most of the students came by train. There were plenty of other nervous freshmen when the up-train got in that evening. And there was at least one, Luther Evanston Smith, you've heard of him, who walked the twenty-one miles from Petersfield with his bundle on his back. None of us were ever allowed to forget about that, especially in later years. I think that every time Lute told about it to someone younger than himself he added another mile."

II

Matt was away for the first two weeks of November, on alumni and fund-raising trips, and came back with creases under his eyes, dyspepsia and a temper as short as a Manx tail. "I cannot spend so much time away and run the College too! I've already given up teaching my course, which is what I enjoyed most, and now I've got this new faculty committee on the natural sciences which will mean an enormous amount of time. Our whole curriculum needs a new look and what we decide now will determine the character of the College for the next decade and longer. This is important, if you please, just as important as money-raising."

"But we need a new library, we must have a new library," I said. "Much as I love the old one, it's an absurd building for a college of eight times the size of the one it was built for. Besides, it's falling down."

"I know. Whatever faculty committees decide to do, it can't be done properly without a new library. We just don't seem to have enough rich relatives."

I had thought that while he was away I would have time for Amos and the History. But the days — and nights — were wiped away by the illness of a child. I spent long hours by the littlest one's bed, and saw the sun rise, and the days grow and fall, and at night Orion wheel high from the eastern hill, my hand upon the small hot body that fought a good fight. "My soul waiteth for the Lord more than they that watch for the morning: I say, more than they that watch for the morning."

During one of those long hours I heard a heifer bawl up the road, and looked out toward the farm nearby. The College still adjoins rural America; but it is no longer as close to it as it was. In the old days when so many students, like Amos himself, came from the farms, the institution was a part of the hill-pastures and the furrowed fields, of a larger community and a different people. Now we have only a few, like Butch; the rest are sons of suburbs and would be hard put to milk a cow. And there were cows on the campus itself too — though only the cows of full professors were allowed this privilege; chickens wandered there, and sometimes a pig, fattening to be butchered at election time. I knew from an old picture that a picket fence ran round the campus, and outside was the tilled land. All of course was a sea of mud in spring, into which animals, students and professors alike sank among the diminishing drifts of dirty snow. Only the two new stone buildings, massive, bare, indicated that this was indeed a different kind of farm.

Agriculture is still the mainstay of the country around us, and the College windows look out upon big black and white cows moving slowly across their pastures. But few people here know or care about what goes on so near to our campus. To be sure, some faculty members in economics or sociology have met with farmers' groups, on marketing and rural problems, and perhaps been of some help, but they don't get into the barns or dirty their feet in the fields.

Amos had taken me one day to call on his cousin Drusilla, who lived on his family's old farm in the next valley. As we drove over the hills the woods were black-purple in the distance, but there was still a golden shimmer on the fields where the cattle grazed in the corn-stubble, the stalks sticking comically from their grinding mouths.

"It all used to be sheep country," mused Amos. "The dairy business only came in in the last hundred years, and at first only for cheese-making. The country was full of little cheese factories and New York State cheese was famous the world over. The big barns were built in those days; there was an enormous one on our place, long since burned down. It was as beautiful as a Romanesque basilica, and I thought it was the largest building on earth when I played in the haymow, at least until one day when my father showed me the College, with Champion Hall looming massive on the hill. I suppose it was that day I decided to go to the College; I looked across the fat backs of our old white mares and knew in my heart that there was no other possibility. What I did not know was that so much of my life would be spent there."

On the far side of the next ridge we turned into a dirt road and drove south, climbing slightly. The sun was warm on our knees and on the long weedy pastures behind the crooked fences. The small farmhouse had been white, but now it was grayed with weather; it was a typical New York State house, the main part with the gable end toward the front, with the ell at right angles, with a small pillared porch. At the side I saw under the eaves the beautiful iron grilles set in tiny windows which are the hallmark of these old houses.

No smoke came from the chimney, and the blinds were drawn. "Cousin Druse just lives in the kitchen"; and I followed him round to the back door through the long grass and sprawling rosebushes.

Cousin Druse was just as fat as Amos was thin; she was a series of circles set one on the other, but somewhere amongst the soft folds and in the very blue eyes I saw kinship, which the smile confirmed.

We sat a long time in the kitchen; there were rockers by the oilcloth-covered table, and we creaked gently as we talked. There was no fire in the black-polished wood stove; an old-fashioned electric heater with round red coils glowed in the corner of the stuffy room. There was a sugar bowl and a vase of spoons on the table; everything was clean but nothing was neat. On the wall were old brown photographs, and by the door into the parlor a wreath in a glass case. While Amos and Druse were exchanging information on recent deaths and illnesses I looked at the wreath. A complicated pattern of flowers and fruits, I saw it was all woven of hair; in letters of hair it said *In Loving Memory of Nettie Whitefield 1879.*

When the necrology was complete Amos said, "We've been working together on the History of the College and talking about the old days when mostly farm boys went there."

"Land yes," said Cousin Druse, "all the boys around here, the ones that were smart enough, went, less they were Methodists, then they went to Syracuse. Amos' father — that was my uncle — couldn't go himself though he wanted to the worst way, because Grandfather died and he had to work the farm. But he was bound and determined that Amos should go, and he and Aunt Ellen pieced along for a good many years so there'd be some money to send him. Of course Aunt Ellen wanted him to be a preacher. But I guess she was satisfied when he got to be a professor, that was just before she died, wasn't it, Amos, that you got to be a full out-and-out Professor?"

Amos nodded. "Druse, when you were a little girl you

lived with Grandma Whitefield in this house. I remember there was a big Bible with covers an inch thick and lots of pictures on the parlor table. But Grandfather had some other books, in the glass top to the rolltop desk, only Grandmother kept them locked up all the time. Do you know what they were?"

"*Paradise Lost*," said Druse, smacking her lips with respect, "and Josephus' *History*, and oh a lot more I don't remember, and of course the doctor book and the horse-doctor book. But I remember Grandmother telling me that when her folks first come here, from Connecticut, after the Revolution, they had in the loghouse only the one Book. They came in oxcarts, then up the river, it took 'em a month, she said, there was a whole passel of 'em together, and cousin Charity Winstead had a baby on the way."

"And they built a school almost right away," said Amos, "a church and a school, and then later an 'academy' — that's how most of our colleges began on the frontier."

Druse made us some coffee, and Amos showed me the old photos and tintypes; even in their faded shadows I could see the shape of a head, a direct look in the eyes, that showed how strong, how persistent this stock must have been, which I saw living before me.

We went back over the hills as the sun set; the last shine caught the spire on the College chapel as we dropped down into our own valley.

III

The College has its own cemetery, almost at the top of the hill, north of the great hemlock at the edge of the woods. The early stones mark the graves of very old divines, or very young students. In the faint November sunshine I sat on one, under the drooping spruce branches, that said *Faithful to his College and his God*. There were many later ones too, and some new ones. Opposite me was the massive granite marker for Blessington Downer, 1843–1913, Professor and Acting President of the College. Beyond was the older one of the Civil War President, Elisha Early.

Faintly I heard the bell from the classrooms below the slope, then doors banging and voices calling. How many hours of classes, of labor with books and boys, lie here below these stones? What was taught and what was learned? Did students then seem to have the same imperviousness of mind, watertight amidst the rich flow of ideas around them; was it so then? And what of those curious and mistaken concepts which these earlier teachers placed before their classes: ideas which we now think are erroneous, ideas which we now know are wrong? What did the students accept, were they misled, perhaps all their lives, because here they were mistaught?

The stone is cold, but even colder is the consequent question: what, of all that we are teaching here today, is mistaken, what is wholly wrong?

The wind picked up among the gravestones, and the spruces spoke softly above them. But there were no other answers. I whistled the dogs and went home.

•

I asked Amos about Blessington Downer.

"In every period of an institution's history," he answered in the formal way with which he sometimes addressed me, as though I were a large class, "some one person becomes the symbol, which people think of when they hear the institution's name. The History of the College is in a way the history of these men. In fact yesterday, at the Faculty Club, Mr. Birnbaum suggested to me that I write the History as a series of biographies. This is an idea which I suspect he got from Carlyle. In any case I do not think it is adequate; surely the total is more that the sum of the parts. But naturally we will spend a good many pages on our great men, and of these Blessington Downer is one of the most picturesque, and was in his day the person who typified the College. Old God-Bless they called him; I was fortunate to have him in several history courses. He taught almost all the history that was given in the College in those days, and some of the literature too. He had been trained in Germany; in fact I think his was the first appearance on our campus of what was then the new style in professors: someone with special training in a special field and with a graduate degree, usually, in those days, from Germany.

"He was a person of enormous vitality, even when I knew him, when he was no longer young. Every minute of his life he was teaching; in the classroom, in his own house, in the street, at Chautauqua in the summers, on the lecture platform all the year round. That was why everyone knew him, all over the state, and thought of him when they thought of the College. He was fifty times more colorful than old President Theobald Stringer. Part of his stock in trade were his mannerisms. If someone asked a foolish question in class, or answered wrongly, he would lay his head on the desk and give heartrending groans. If the answer continued to be wrong he would lie on the floor and writhe in agony. New students used to answer badly to see the show, but they soon found out every groan meant half a point lower in their marks so they gave it up. When he met students on the campus, and he knew them all by name, he would not say 'How do you do?' he would say 'What are you reading?' I think he learned this from Wilamowitz in Germany, but it was equally effective here."

Amos laughed and looked out of the window. "You can just see the corner of his house from here, the big square red-brick one." It was the house where the head of the philosophy department lives now, with a flat roof edged with a heavy white cornice like cake frosting.

"When I first came here I thought it was the handsomest house I had ever seen. And Downer fitted it: like him it was big and well-proportioned and of its period. In those days we had a custom, which now is fortunately out of style: after an athletic victory or a class frolic, we would go about town at night and get a professor or two out of bed and call for a speech." Amos coughed drily. "There were some faculty members who did not care for this kind of thing, as you can imagine. But Old God-Bless loved it. I remember well the midnight before my commencement; we had had a very gay evening, and we ended up in front of the Downers'. He climbed out of that oval hall window in answer to our calls and stood on the flat roof of the front porch, in a voluminous old-fashioned nightshirt that became him like a toga. I can see him now: it was bright moonlight, and some of it came through the thick maples and made brilliant patches on the white trim of the house and on our faces below. Oh I don't remember what he said, but I know it made us laugh, and we went away applauding and saying Good Old Downder and Blitzen just the same as ever."

"You must write it down," I said, "it must go into the History." And when I went out past the red-brick house I could clearly see Acting President and Professor Downer on his porch roof in a nightshirt.

IV

When the snow fell I thought of the wartime years when we first came to the College. Our first commencement was in December, when the seniors who would have graduated

in June went off to war. I can see them now, performing
the torch ceremony which is usually held by a green lake
under leafy maples; but then, like a scene from a Russian
novel, took place in snow and ice. The black-robed figures
stood on the frozen bank, tossing their flaring torches not
into the water but onto the ice, singing their song through
the drifting snow.

It was hard to realize the students of today were only
children then; the war was only names to them. But then,
year after year, we saw the boys we knew leave month
after month, for far places and uncertain fates. Sorrow is
very concentrated in a college whose lifeblood is the lifeblood of young men.

Amos showed me in an old newspaper, locally published, an account of the students going off to another war.
As soon as the news of Fort Sumter reached the campus,
with President Lincoln's call to arms, the President of the
College called a meeting of both town and gown. The
band played, President Early declaimed, a solo was sung
by the soprano from the Methodist Church, and the call
for volunteers was given. I gathered from the account that
there was no immediate rush to arms. But finally a tall
lanky boy from the College stood up and was followed by
several others from the town. Many more went later from
the College, and the institution had a hard time to survive.
Money was scarce, students were few, and the whole at-
tention of the country was centered on the conflict. There
was then no naval training program to keep the campus

alive, such as we had had in World War II when boys in uniform swarmed all over the College and the hard-worked faculty taught strange subjects. But after the Civil War it did not seem that the little institution could survive. There were few donors and few students; the war had taken them or impoverished them. There was no money for books, there was no money for salaries, even though the entire faculty consisted of four men, including the President. The women of the church made clothes for such students as there were, but there was no money for stoves for the new building completed just before the war.

But Early was not daunted; out he went on the road and, somehow or other, in churches, in public meetings, in the offices of rich men in New York, he raised enough to keep the place together, until the seventies and eighties brought more money and more students as the state and the country expanded.

"How did he do it?" I asked Amos. "He taught full time, and it took him days to get to New York instead of hours as it does Mathias. And since he was a minister as well he must have had to preach some of the time."

Amos shook his head. "They were giants in those days. The others must have taken his place in classroom and pulpit. And don't forget there were only about forty or fifty students, and not all of them were on campus at the same time. They used to attend college as long as their money held out, then leave to work, then come back." He smiled, "Class scheduling must have been complicated."

Before I left I asked Amos if he had manuscript that I could start typing. He said rather fussily that he did not have any in final form yet. He turned quite pink, right up into his short white hair. It occurred to me that perhaps he had not written any of the History yet.

V

December was as always a month full to the brim of plans, questions, parties, doings, bright days and long dark nights, with the snow over all. Matt spent most of it away from the campus, going to New York like Elisha Early and for the same reason, to the west for alumni meetings, to Washington for a conference. Many of the questions and doings came to me instead: what color to paint the lobby of the Student Center? (anything but institutional green). What date for the faculty intersemester party? Whom shall we invite to speak at the annual faculty dinner? (I suggested Amos, but they told me though he was excellent in class he was a poor public speaker.) And where shall we put the swans for the winter now that the lake is wholly frozen?

Old Mrs. Professor Johansen died at last and I went to the funeral. Young Mrs. Assistant Professor Vernon had a new baby and I called with a gift. Mr. Sullivan, who had been head groundsman for so long, was in the hospital with a broken hip and I went to see him, with a small pot of lily-of-the-valley pips that would bloom for Christmas; he and I together had planted hundreds and hundreds of daffodils about the campus.

One evening a student came, eager to talk to the President. He was so full of his problems he stayed and talked to me for an hour and a half by the fire in the living room, while I worked on the navy-blue sweater with the white reindeer pattern which I had to have done for the nine-year-old for Christmas. His name was Paul Lightwood, a sophomore and a non-fraternity man, and he was badly afflicted by Wanderlust and Weltschmerz and all the things with German names that torture the young.

"I don't think I'm getting anywhere in college, I want to leave. I want to go abroad, not just to travel, but to do something. I want to help somebody." He seemed to talk in italics. "The world is such a mess and I am sitting around studying philosophy and math and the history of Western man, playing a little hockey and watching TV and arguing about Life. What good is it? I feel so futile."

He was a long boy, not yet filled out, with beautiful dark eyes and the usual spots. I asked him about his marks.

"Good. There's no problem there, that's not why I want to get away. But what do marks mean?"

I asked him what his family thought of his idea of leaving.

"Oh, they think I'm crazy. Dad has saved all the money to put me through, and he wants to see *results*. And Mother — well, I think she's worrying about how to explain it to her friends if I leave college in the middle." He laughed at that, but not very much. I asked him if he had talked to his tutor.

"Yes, he says go ahead if you want to, you can always come back later. But do I want to?"

I gave him a Coke and a doughnut, and we went all over it again: the fire snaps, a log drops, I am starting the feet of the reindeer, there seem to be five. Outside I hear the plow go by, it must be snowing again. There is a yell from upstairs, "Mom, I can't find my pajamas." I yell back without losing the stitch-count, "It's laundry day, take clean ones out of the drawer."

At last Paul said, interlacing his long fingers, "I feel it's the most important point in my life, what I decide now will decide my whole career."

And I said, but not aloud, every point decides your whole career, but things are not as irrevocable as you think: relax. Aloud I said, "You'll have to brood over it some more, Paul. When the President gets back I'll tell him about our conversation. But you know he's not going to tell you what to do. You know who has to do that, don't you?"

He nodded and started to take his leave; I had not done anything for him, but he was happier for my receptive ear. We chatted a little more and at last he got to the door; all winter blew in as it opened. The black spaniel ran out with him into the new snow. I went back, poked up the fire, put away the knitting, got myself a beer and sat think-

ing about Paul and 1199 others, and about the parents behind them. Each problem is monumental to each. And in
a way of course Paul was right, this moment now does
determine the years to come.

The cocker banged at the door and ran in like Simpkin
shaking his ears; his night-black coat was embroidered
with white and his feet scalloped in snow.

·

I told Amos about Paul when I snatched an hour next
day to work in his study by the fire. The snow was blow-
ing horizontally outside and Amos' eyes were on it as he
said, "The river is the same, only the water changes." He
stood up and walked about the room; when I heard the
little cough I knew the lecture was about to begin and put
down my papers.

"I sometimes think," said Amos, "that to live and work
in a college is like standing still in the middle of a road
where an army of young men move endlessly toward the
front. We face them, our backs to their future; on the
right and on the left they pass us slowly, in loose order. As
they go by we learn their names, and speak to them; for us
they have a smile, an answer, sometimes a sullen look. But
our moment with them is brief, and their eyes, resting for a
short space upon us and upon the books and tools we hand
them, soon move toward the road ahead."

His look, out of the window, seemed to see that army.

"To them, with the different chronometers of youth,
that meeting seems much longer, indeed it is about a fifth

of their lives. But to us, as college generation succeeds generation, it grows shorter each year. It is difficult enough to know any other human being well; but to know one from intermittent contacts over forty months is impossible, especially when the object of knowledge moves, changes and grows from moment to moment, like a living cell under a microscope.

"This is what makes it so chancy to give a student advice — which is a chancy business at best, whoever the recipient. It is only the recurrent repetitive nature of both problems and reactions in the lives of young men from eighteen to twenty-two that emboldens us to offer some guidelines. Each boy's problem is new, unique to him; but it is a brother to the problems of thousands of other unique problems presented, analyzed and often solved upon this campus. Each face within these ranks that pass is new; we forget or disregard that individuality at our peril. But we have learned through our own journeys words to say to each, not always different words, nor the same words with the same effects. All we can hope is that the word we say and the moment upon the road may be not without value to us both."

His words were so real to me at that moment that I seemed to see the procession too, and said softly, "Yes, that's what we're here for." He turned back to me and I could see he had forgotten he was not alone. How many lectures, how many wise words fell unheard within that old study when I was not there?

~ III

I was pleased to see Amos at the midwinter tea at the Faculty Club. He had been much of a recluse in the past years; Mrs. Johansen had told me that he never went out to social affairs after his wife's death.

"They were wholly devoted to each other, and after the little boy died they were never out of each other's sight. We hardly expected Amos to live after Rose died, but he has a tough country streak in him, and he survived and has made a sort of life for himself. Not that he's ever gotten over it, of course."

He was standing with Longridge of the English Department, and I joined them with some remark about the weather.

" 'The season of snows and sins . . . the light that loses, the night that wins,' " quoted Longridge, stirring a cup of tea that seemed to be half sugar.

Amos pricked up his ears. "I thought Swinburne was out of fashion nowadays."

"My dear Dr. Whitefield, he's so out of fashion that

now he's all the rage. It won't be long before we'll be having Browning societies again."

Amos chuckled. "We had one here when I was in college, made up of both students and faculty. We met in the evening at Professor Johansen's and took turns reading aloud. Mrs. Johansen was very young and very beautiful; when she read 'stung by the splendour of a sudden thought' we held our breaths. It was heady stuff, you know, we used to come out of those meetings into the cold starry night reeling as though we had been drinking."

Dr. Stanislaus came up with a plate of pink cookies. "My dear Madam," — he always calls me Madam which gives me a curious feeling — "my dear Madam, may I offer you sustenance. You must need strength, I saw you striding along the drive."

He was shouting at me, but I was not perturbed, for Stanislaus always shouts; they say in Winstead Hall you can hear him lecturing three floors up. I only hope that what he shouts to his classes is of more import than his conversation.

I saw little Mrs. Jaffe wide-eyed in a corner and moved to chat with her, taking Dr. Montgomery along with me. Dr. Montgomery collected bits of rare bric-a-brac and frail objets d'art, and I thought Mrs. Jaffe, even pregnant, would appeal to him.

Mrs. Birnbaum was pouring; it was apparently Chemistry's turn. As she filled my cup I asked after her litter of fox-faced children. Birnbaum, the head of the Department, is one of the best scientists we have ever had on this campus; he is red-haired, slanty-eyed, and all the children look exactly like him. Good scientists, especially of his stature, are hard to come by, and hard to keep, in small colleges, hence my solicitude for his family; besides, I like Mrs. Birnbaum and I am fond of the little foxes. Through the account of measles, teeth, and one broken arm, I heard two voices behind me and, turning, surprised a look that startled me. It was young Mrs. Rodd, wife of the Assistant Professor of Sociology, talking to Mannheim, the math man whom we have had all the trouble with. There might be more trouble, I thought, as I looked at her sulky and beautiful face, the great eyes, the discontented mouth, the high bosom. Rodd, her husband, whom I did not see at the party, was currently engaged on a book on family life.

But the President's wife must be all three monkeys in one, and I went back to Amos and Longridge with my cup in hand. They were talking about Tuckerman Butterweck, Class of '17.

"They say he's made a fantastic amount of money," Longridge was saying, with a typical faculty preoccupation.

Amos had a way of smiling without opening his mouth, just pulling up the right side of his cheek, with an effect at once kind and sardonic. "He was a very poor boy when he came to college," he said, "but he always knew what he wanted."

"It must have been money for one thing," said Longridge. "I hear he's selling his business for an incredible amount."

"He was a wonderfully persistent boy," said Amos thoughtfully, "He was not a good scholar, but he never gave up. And he believed in his luck. I think that was his real secret. He used to say to me, 'Dr. Whitefield, I am a very lucky fellow, and I am going to be lucky all my life.' It was almost a religious principle with him. And you know if you believe in your luck that strongly, you have it."

"I hope he will give the College some of his 'luck,'" I said.

II

As we moved backward, in Amos' quaint plan for the History, we left behind the days he had known at first hand, and I hoped for fewer reminiscences, much as I enjoyed them, so that we might get ahead with the work.

It was no peaceful period, the eighties and seventies: years of postwar reconstruction, great political activity, railroad building and the development of the West, years of panic and depression as well.

"Things were moving in education too," said Amos, turning over the course plans for those years. "Here in 1888 for the first time Greek and Latin are not required. French and German are allowed instead, but they 'rec-

ommend strongly that all students, in the scientific course
as well as the classical course, take Latin.' And it is per-
mitted to take zoology instead of mathematics; that was
quite a change, for math was a pillar of the curriculum in
the early days. Ah, here's a whole page of science courses
taught by Eben Sanderson. I remember Professor Sanderson when he was very old. But they said that when he first
came to the campus he was like a breath of fresh wind
from the outside world. A man of immense energy, he
taught half-a-dozen subjects — mathematics, zoology, biology, physics, astronomy; he had a course in surveying
too, and the students could hardly keep up with him as he
bounded over the countryside. There was little laboratory
equipment for any of the sciences in those days, but Professor Sanderson did his best to fill the lack. He himself
made equipment in his workshop; he was a Yankee from
Vermont, ingenious and clever with his hands, and he
taught the students not only the principles of science but
how to manufacture the lab equipment to prove them.
Many of his students, men whom I have known, went on
to be successful in one branch of science or another: teachers, inventors, research workers, like Bill Hammersted at
Chicago who has done so much in biology, and Ayer, the
physicist at Harvard. Most of them are dead now, but I
am sure they handed on some of the zest for learning and
discovering which old Sandy gave them. Perhaps —" —
he looked across at me — "perhaps old Sandy is our candidate for the Man of the College in his time.

"But the classics were by no means forgotten, although they had to compete with the novelty and excitement of what Sanderson taught. And I am afraid they were often taught in very dull fashion — too much grammar and too much composition of indifferent prose in Greek and Latin. But —" — and his eyes lighted as they always did when he talked of the classics — "they learned many many lines of the old poets by heart, and to some students it was a lifelong treasure of beauty. It was told in my day that Professor Jepson, who taught Greek at that time, took his classes outdoors whenever the weather was fine and made them recite Homer in the open air, in that grove of maples behind Champion Hall. He said that was the way Greek was meant to be enjoyed, out-of-doors; but I am afraid our climate, less agreeable than Homer's, did not permit this very often."

He went back to his papers and I to mine, but shortly he was off on a new track.

"Courses weren't taught by lectures, you know; that didn't become popular until almost my time. The students had to recite from the textbook — see, here it says in 1887, 'The method of instruction is a system of patient oral drill supplemented by a carefully prepared course of written review.'" He shook his head. "They had to stay awake, and had to perform, but I wonder if they learned from that parroting."

I thought about it as I walked home in the early January dark. There were lights in all the buildings on the hill, in classrooms and laboratories, in the library. The November question returned to my mind: teaching is endlessly going on in this place, boys are passing endlessly through these halls: is the process successful? And what is success?

III

Even in late January the sun could be seen to be slowly crawling back to our land. On the snow it was almost dazzling in the below-zero air. The shadow of the snow-fence was dark-blue on a drift already barred with ripples by the wind, making a delicate cross-hatching in light and shade. I felt a definite warmth on my back as I went down the hill to Amos'.

But I was worrying about the History. I had done a good deal of research on the periods where Satterwell's cards were blank or missing, and Amos had been working, he said, steadily. But as yet no manuscript had appeared for me to type, and I was shy about asking him for it again. That day however I had decided to do so. But when I went in I found that Connard Leach was there. He often dropped in to visit, and the two of them were sitting over the fire as though it was the potbellied stove in the country store. I said I would come again another time, but Amos called me in.

"Come and sit down. We're working on the history together, Connard, and that's what you and I are, local history."

I knew the two of them had been friends since Connard the sophomore dunked Amos the freshman in the annual water-fight. Like many another of the local old families he was a devoted alumnus. It was his great-great-great-grandfather who trapped the swift Canowenda behind a dam and set her to work for him grinding grain and sawing timber. In fact the settlement was called Leach's Mills in those days. The old stones and wheels are still now, but Connard ran a feed and a farm supply store in the big old building whose core is still the stone and timber set by Job Leach just as the nineteenth century was born.

Connard was a man of substance and a pillar of the Republican party, but you never would have guessed it to look at him; his long old coat flapped on his skinny frame and his trousers were full of little holes burned from the embers of his pipe. He and Amos were in the middle of one of their violent political discussions, for Amos was one of those rare birds, a native New York State rural Democrat. The sparks were flying, and I was reminded of the first time I heard them at it. It was in the post office as they looked at their newspapers, and I thought they would end at each other's throats. But after five minutes' fireworks they went off amiably together as though nothing had happened. George Philbrick, the postmaster, winked at me from behind the window, "Always like that, been going at each other for fifty years, best friends there are."

Now, having damned the daylights out of the administration and the opposition respectively, they broke off abruptly, and Amos said mildly, "We're just beginning on the material of the eighteen-thirties and eighteen-forties now, Connard, the time of the Big Quarrel."

"My great-grandfather's time," said Connard, "I remember his telling me about it when I was a boy. How different the history of this town would have been if they had moved the College away then, as they tried to."

I had been doing some reading about the Quarrel: a nearby city, wanting a university, had suggested the College move there as a nucleus, and had offered a large sum as an inducement. It must have been tempting, for the little institution was having a hard time to survive. And many wanted to accept, thinking it the easier and perhaps the only way. But there were others, who had grown up with it on this site, and seen its roots grow into the hill, and foresaw a better future here than there. A character and an ethos of its own was what they wanted, and not to be swallowed up in a rapidly developing city, at the mercy of the city fathers and — as they said — the religion of commerce.

The campus was split from side to side, and for a time it seemed as though it would destroy itself with dissension, and neither go nor stay.

"Of course the village wanted it to stay," said Connard. "They knew which side their bread was buttered on. Though of course, in those days, they foresaw a great

future for the town too, and they were hardheaded enough
to realize the College was an important part of it. They
would have been disappointed to see the town now — a
tiny rural center with no growth in population or wealth
for the last two or three decades. But at the time they put
up some money, you know, several thousand dollars as I
remember, to keep the College here — a huge sum for this
little place in those days."

"But there were many of the faculty," said Amos,
"which of course means a handful — but the more influen-
tial ones, who perhaps felt even then the isolation here.
They wanted the advantages of a city, and the money
looked very enticing; perhaps salaries could be raised
above the usual three or four hundred dollars a year. You
know when the new President was hired in 1865, even
then they offered him a salary of $600."

"People on opposite sides of the Quarrel did not speak to
each other on the street," said Connard. "My folks contrib-
uted to the Keeping Fund, as they called it, and Doc Hei-
denbach, who was President for a short time then, and
wanted very much to move, wouldn't speak to them, even
though they were old friends."

"I wonder if any subject of controversy could split the
College so widely now," mused Amos. "It doesn't seem
possible. There is a unity here now, developed over the
years — our Ethos if you please," glancing at me, "that
seems to me to preclude any such quarrel."

But I was thinking about what Matt had told me the day

before, and I knew there was indeed a possibility that
might explode upon us. And no institution, no matter how
old, how firm, how homogeneous can develop an immunity
to schism.

•

Matt had been in New York and came back with a
baffled look on his face. It was a Sunday, and when in the
afternoon the kids had all gone skating we sat in the sunny
windowseat over coffee; he said abruptly, "Tuckerman
Butterweck wants to give the College three million dollars."

I jumped so sharply that the cat flew out of my lap with
an angry miaow. But he went on quickly, "He wants to
build a Tower of Trade."

My heart went back to its normal place or a little lower.
In the split-second pace of the brain I had built, between
his two statements, the handsomest, most commodious,
most efficient college library in the State of New York. "A
what?" I said.

"You heard me. A Tower of Trade, housing the G.
Tuckerman Butterweck School of Commerce."

He told me about the interview. I was remembering
the round pink-cheeked face, the short stalwart body, the
pleasant smile — and also the hardness in the eyes, the
note of steel in the voice. We did not know him well, because his import-export business took him mostly abroad;
but we knew of course that he was very rich. Now,

apparently, as I had heard at the Club, he was selling his business at an enormous profit and needed to make large gifts.

"He said he had had this idea in mind for some time — though it's the first anyone connected with the College has heard of it — and he's decided to 'put the College on the map' with a school for training in foreign business."

"But — but this College is not the place for that kind of thing!"

"Of course not. Whatever merit the idea has, and I think it may have a good deal, it belongs on a university campus, in connection with or part of a graduate school of business. But Tuck cares only for this College, he got all his education here, and this is where he wants it to be."

"Can't we or somebody persuade him to give it for something else — a library for instance?"

"Not Tuck. I tried. He wants the G. Tuckerman Butterweck Tower of Trade. It's going to be Gothic, too."

"What are you talking about?"

"That's right. He's seen somewhere, I don't know where, in Pisa or Pittsburgh or Yale a great dominating Gothic tower, and that's what he wants on our campus, on the hill above the chapel, where it can be seen practically from Albany to Buffalo."

"But," I said in a very small voice, "that's where we're going to build the new library."

"Oh no we're not," he said roughly, which showed me how he felt, "only Tuck's Tower. Three million dollars is three million dollars and I don't see the trustees turning it away."

The kids came in pink-cheeked from skating, shouting, "We're starving when do we eat?"

IV

I was just about to leave, next day, to go to the library and thence to Amos with some material on the 1850s, when the doorbell rang. I fought down the desire to sneak out the back way and answered it. It was Stan, my helper from last year, whom I had got to know very well, better, it seemed, than I would ever get to know Butch. He was an earnest boy with an unexpectedly merry smile; he was on a scholarship which he was always just about to lose, for his marks were never very good.

There was no merry smile that day; he looked pale and sad. "Could I talk to you? I've got an hour between classes, if you're free. Or I'll come back some other time."

I brought him into my study and swept the to-be-filed stacks of papers off the sofa. The sun was bright on my Roman hyacinths on the windowsill; they were just coming into bloom, the green buds stretching into delicate bells, the sleeping green turning into brilliant white.

"I'm in trouble, ma'am. I have to talk to somebody." His fingers moved in and out. "I've done wrong and now I'm in trouble."

My mind ran rapidly over the possibilities: cheating on a paper, something about a car (scholarship boys are not allowed cars), a girl?

It was the last. I knew her, in fact she had stayed in the house a year ago when she visited Stan for a weekend: a big-eyed little creature, shy and dark, with small hands and feet.

He looked down, staring at the yellow rug, moving his feet. I had met his mother several times, when she had driven him to the campus; hard-working, her face lined and bright-eyed, intensely religious. The father was dead. She was violently ambitious for the boy, he was to be a minister. This girl came from the same town and they had been in high school together.

"I want to get married," he burst out, "Sukey and I always talked of getting married some day. It's not as though I didn't want to marry her, or she me. But there's no money, and Mother will be — shattered. I know I can't keep my scholarship, I've got exams next week and I can't study, I call Sukey every night."

It all came pouring out, the weekend, the long drive in the snowy night, the car — Our big retriever, who is very sensitive to human voices, and was very fond of Stan, got up from his corner and stood at his knee, the great feathered tail swinging slowly. The boy fingered the soft ears as he talked.

"First," I said, "is she sure?"

He nodded dumbly.

"And how about *her* family?"

We talked on and on, turning the problem over and over, trying to plan something constructive to rebuild what he considered the ruins of his life: what would be best, for him, for Sukey, for their families? Again and again the theme recurred, 'I was wrong, I did wrong, I must be punished,' and I realized how strongly the mother's teachings were embedded, how different his attitude was from other boys I knew. Not only his life but his soul was injured, and his spiritual agony clouded his mind and made it hard for him to think of Sukey or to plan rationally.

At last the hour was up. "You will have to talk to the Dean. I don't know what he will say, but when you can see where you are going you must do it." The pain in his eyes was so great that I felt, like the dog, that I must try to provide comfort. But I had none for him but the comfort of a sympathetic ear.

The boys came bounding in from school, hungry for lunch, glad to see Stan, who was their favorite ball player. He pulled himself together; "Thank you for listening."

"Come back," I said, "please come back, and we'll talk again, Stan."

The boys leaped upon him, there was a scrimmage in the front hall with the dog helping joyfully. The chandeliers rattled, and when it was all sorted out Sam went away with a little color in his face.

•

Matt called from the office to say he had decided to go to New York to meet with Mr. Butterweck again. Would I please pack a bag and bring it to the office at once so that he could catch the two o'clock plane? He said that the Chairman of the Board of Trustees had reported that he too had been to see Mr. Butterweck, in an effort to turn his mind in other directions; but the fact remained clear that Mr. B. wanted a School of Commerce in a tall tower on the rise beyond the chapel, a Collegiate Gothic Tower, the G. Tuckerman Butterweck Tower of Trade. Tuck did not argue back, Matt said, with him or with the Chairman; he just sat there and let the words wash over him. And he was hurt that his magnificent sum, his magnificent idea were not immediately and enthusiastically accepted. He kept saying, "But this is what you need, this is the important thing for the College to have. This will make the campus really distinguished, it will be known all over the world, like the Washington Monument, like the Leaning Tower of Pisa."

v

I had wondered often, as I sat in Amos' house, with its masculine disorders superimposed upon its basic neatness and charm, what Mrs. Whitefield was like. She died years before we came to the College, so that I never heard much about her. But there was in the little white-pillared house a lingering warmth, a sweet aroma of love and care which I could see still, not only in its rooms but about Amos, and which told me that here must have been someone as charming as her name, Rose Freemantle Whitefield.

I came in rather late the next afternoon, after some duty calls, and made tea, which we drank by the study fire.

"My dear, you do not know how much I appreciate this in my lonely house."

I was getting to know him so well I could see it was not to be a History day, and since I wanted to know about her I turned on purpose the key to that door. "How long is it since Mrs. Whitefield died?"

We sat there for an hour or more, while the light fell behind the larches; the church clock struck and struck again, and I heard the students shouting in a snowball fight. But Amos and I were on the campus of fifty years ago.

He had not met Rose until his senior year. She was the daughter of the new Professor of History, Lawrence Freemantle. In the late summer they moved into this very house; it was painted yellow then, with a porch all the way round under the columns. Amos had come back to the campus early, to work in the Dean's office after a summer on the farm, and saw Murphy's van with the big gray team at the door. Dr. Freemantle was a very tall man, bald-headed; he never seemed to have much control over his limbs, and at that moment was struggling with a heavy Morris chair.

"May I help you, sir?" Amos took the legs and they got it inside easily. There was a girl in the hall and when they got the chair in the right place he took his cap off and the professor introduced himself and her. "And this is my daughter Rose."

Amos thought he had never seen eyes that danced so. Her head came about to his chin and she looked up at him smiling. "You must come and see us when we are settled, Mr. Whitefield."

"I would like to. But I'm not leaving yet." He helped Murphy with the sofa, then Mrs. Freemantle asked him to bring in the box of lamp-chimneys, as she did not trust either her husband or Murphy with them. But Amos was looking at Rose as she dusted the scrollwork of the sofa and hit the corner of the box on the doorpost and cracked one chimney. "We laughed about it for years," said Amos, "and she laughed then. I can hear her now."

They spent most of his senior year together. In the fall he had taken her canoeing, up-river; it was a specially beautiful fall, he said, with the little poplars along the bank golden, and behind, the great maples scarlet along the edges of the mown fields. Rose had lived in the city most of her life, and Amos told her about the farm and showed her the fox's burrow and the beaver's dam.

On warm Saturdays the little river would be full of canoes and rowboats. Sometimes a group would paddle upstream, then tie all the boats together and drift back down, singing, to the boathouse and a feed on its balcony above the water. Amos thought he had never been so happy, and Rose was enchanted with this life, and with this boy with the sky-blue eyes.

And in the winter when the snow came he took her sleigh-riding. She told him about sleighing in Central Park, the beautiful horses and elegant rigs full of fashionable people, the races and crash-ups and excitement. Amos looked ruefully at the shaggy nag from Herman's Livery and touched him with the whip.

"But I like this better," said Rose quickly. She wore a scarlet knitted cap and the curls blew back around it as the horse quickened into a trot. It was snowing and ahead of them the hemlock woods above the Canowenda were blurred and dark. The hoofs were soundless in the snow and there was only a whisper from the runners. The road sloped up through the woods and as the horse slowed Amos set the whip in the socket and put his arm around her; he had never seen anything so pretty in his whole life as the snowflakes clinging to the dark hair, melting on the rose-touched skin.

"By spring there was an understanding between us, and I bought her a light canoe paddle for an engagement present, with her initials painted in gold filigree on the blade."

But of course it was a long time before they could be married. At last Amos got an instructor's job in a city college, and they were married in the chapel by President Stringer himself and set off to make a home in a room and a half in a basement in New York.

By the time he had got the appointment to his own College, Dr. Freemantle had moved to Massachusetts, and Rose and Amos took the old house. They ripped off the Victorian porch, painted the Greek columns and the house white, and planted the garden.

"We had thirty years together in this house," he said, "and forty-four of married life." He brought me a miniature from his desk: she smiled at me, I had never seen eyes more full of love. "I had this done after the boy was born, so that he should have it one day." He turned away to the window. "After he died she did not look like that. But we had each other, and we were happy."

•

When I went out into the snow I saw that the College was full of girls. I had been so far away in time with Amos I had forgotten it was Winter Party weekend. There were girls everywhere, hand-in-hand with the boys on the snowy walks, as though a great flock of strange birds had suddenly alighted among us, chattering, singing, preening, watching everything with their bright eyes.

Next day I had six of them staying in the house: they were all pretty and well-mannered, but the prettiest and the most well-mannered was a Negro girl from Boston, the date of a boy I had got to know well on a joint committee. Butch too had gotten up his courage to ask me if I would put up his girl, a charming little thing who told me she wanted to be a missionary. I was just about to ask her why when Butch came in, his hair on end, his nose red with the cold. And as they went off together, smiling at each other, I thought of Amos and his Rose.

VI

The question of the acceptance of the Butterweck gift was to be decided at the February trustees' meeting, which is always held in New York. I was so anxious about it that I could think of nothing else; I was hoping that some compromise could be reached, some way found to avert the Tower that leaned over us. I called Amos to say I could not come that day; suddenly our History seemed unimportant. What did it matter what the College of yesterday was like? What it was to be like in the future was the overpowering question.

If the Tower of Trade became a reality the campus would assume a new and different character; all that Matt had worked for in his years at the College, his efforts to make it the best liberal arts college in the state would be if not vitiated at least radically changed. I knew he felt so strongly that he might indeed resign, and leave, we would all leave. Could I love another college? I looked up the hill to the spire of the chapel above the bare-branched trees, to the hemlock tree whose high black head showed beyond the buildings. The Tower would dwarf the spire, the tree, the College and our hearts.

•

When Matt came back at last I saw at once that the battle had been a hard one and the issue was still in doubt. There were many on the Board who felt that this was an inappropriate gift; there were others who thought, with Mr. Butterweck, that it "is just what the College needs"; but without exception they were unwilling to turn down three million dollars. Mostly they had persuaded themselves that it would be possible to set up the School of Commerce, build the Tower, and yet keep the College the way it has been, the way they want it. Matt felt that these goals were wholly incompatible. "And it would be wicked," he said to me with vehemence, "it would be downright immoral to spend all that money on something that is not needed here, that indeed would be destructive here, when we have so many other enormous needs — endowed chairs to attract great teachers, a new science building to keep our sciences up to date, most of all the new library."

He got up and stalked about the room, white with anger and distress, and I knew that I was looking at the symbol which Amos and I had talked about, the person who is the College, the helmsman and the shield. My heart turned over as he sank wearily into the big chair. "Well," he said dully, "the trustees will discuss it in a meeting with the faculty, and later with the Alumni Council. None of this will do any good, but at least no one can say he didn't have a chance to put in his word."

So far the proposed gift had been, supposedly, a secret confined to the administration and the board of trustees. But in usual campus fashion everyone was talking about it, everyone had an opinion, so it would be good to get it out in the open. But our hearts were heavy as we dressed for a dinner with a visiting lecturer and an evening devoted to the problems of Formosa: could they be worse than ours?

~IV

I drove over the hills to the county seat to look up some of the early deeds of land given to the College. It was the first of March, and the sunlight was renewed and rejoicing. The snow was still very deep, as high as the car in some places along the road, but the sap buckets were out. A good season, I thought, with all this snow and sun, and nights near zero; the high branches feel the warmth and the roots are drinking. I used to feel it was cruel to bleed the maple trees, but now, calloused or perhaps more aware of true cruelties, I watch without a pang the slow drip from the spout and think only of how good it will taste. Do we not ourselves offer sap, not to the trees to be sure, but to our fellows?

Although it was late afternoon when I drove back, after the hours in the archives, the light struck me like a blow. The wide hills rolled slowly up before me, clear and shining in their winter coats, set with red barns and small white houses below the brown-purple woods and the blue sky. As I came near home the light turned sapphire and amethyst on the snow, and the eastern sky before me melted into pale coral; the last sun lay level on the fields where the tree shadows made blue lace veils. To be alive, I thought, as I came down into our own valley, cedar-studded, where far away gleamed the gold grace note of the chapel spire, to be alive in the United States of America, in Canowenda County, on March the first at four o'clock in the afternoon: no matter what happens, to see this light upon the snow.

The larches looked awake as I crossed the river and came into town. I stopped to market, and felt kindly toward everyone, and spoke agreeably to all, and bought two boxes of candy in the American Store for my children.

•

But when Mathias came home that evening from his latest meeting with the Executive Committee of the trustees he had no good news. They were ready to accept the gift of the Tower if Tuck could not be persuaded to give the money for any other purpose, such as the Library. The faculty, with typical aspiration toward the impossible, voted not quite unanimously in favor of persuading him to do this, and were now drawing up a petition to this effect. The undercurrents were running very strongly amongst them, and it was certain that if the School of Commerce was to be built many of the best would resign. Matt reported this to the Executive Committee, stressing how difficult and dangerous it is to go against the faculty, which on this issue was more united than we had ever seen it. But the Committee cannot — and indeed I could understand it — cannot bring themselves to turn away three million dollars.

After the faculty meeting the whole campus was buzzing like a hollow tree full of bees. We feared some kind of publicity that might defeat the whole project, that is, make Mr. Butterweck decide to give his money to the Home for Retired Methodist Ministers or the Baseball Museum. The danger of being stung was increasing daily.

There was to be a meeting of the Alumni Council later in the month, and in the meantime we invited Tuckerman to come for the weekend, to stay with us. "He is quite willing to come," said Mathias, "but he will not listen."

But perhaps, I thought, we can show him what we mean, how we care, what we want for the College. Maybe the donors of those old deeds would have liked an enormous Gothic Tower housing a School of Commerce on their land; but I doubt it.

II

I went to Amos' to work on the material for the 1840s, and we fell to laughing over the entries in the "Steward's Day Book and Journal" for those years. On one page were the items:

*$2.57 being the Amount of Nelson's Bill for Instruction in
Elocution and paid towards the Teacher's Board
    Part Load of Hay last August was not charged say 8/
  50 Sheep Driven here some 4 or 5 weeks Since to have
What they were worth should think 8*

I asked Amos about the prices and he got to talking about
the early days, when almost everything the family used
was supplied by the farm, and what small surplus there
was went in trade at the store in Leach's Mills or was sold,
like this, to the College to feed the students. And before I
really knew what had happened we had slipped back
twenty-seven hundred years and he was telling me about
farming in Hesiod's day.

"Hesiod was really a farmer, first and last, though he
was a poet by profession and I think a moralist by persua-
sion. But the *Works and Days* shows that he was, or at
least had been, a true dirt farmer." He picked up the
Greek text which was never far from his hand. "Listen to
this: 'When the time comes to plow, get to work, both you
and your men, everybody, and work through the plowing
season whether it's wet or dry. Get up early and get going,
so your fields may be full.' He talks about work all the
time — it's a sort of a letter to his lazy brother Perses:
here, 'The gods have put sweat between us and virtue,' and
'There's no disgrace in work, the disgrace is in idleness,'
and so on and on. I think he had that fear of poverty and
hunger which is built into every poor farmer — what they
call nowadays the marginal farmer; I think all farming

was pretty marginal in Hesiod's Boeotia. In fact in one place he says of his home town, 'It's bad in winter and uncomfortable in summer and no good any of the time.'" Amos laughed, riffling the pages. "I used to feel that way about my own village sometimes when I was a boy following the plow and thinking about the city. But there are other pleasanter things in this book that remind me of my youth. Hesiod says when he's talking about the winter: 'Don't go into the smithy and join the crowd gossiping around the fire, there's too much to do at home.' I remember well that enticing warmth and companionship about the forge, when it was too cold to work outside; the look of the red iron and the smell of smoke and horse."

"Actually," I said, "I suppose rural life and farming weren't too different in Boeotia from the early days in these hills."

"Those two times were more alike than present-day farming and the kind I knew as a child." Amos shook his head. "Much of the advice that Hesiod gave would have made sense to my grandfather over the hill. But I'm afraid that neither Grandfather nor Hesiod could cope with farming nowadays — I've looked at some of these machines that Connard sells."

He went on to talk of Hesiod's influence on Virgil — whom he thought less of as a dirt farmer — and my mind wandered to those early days of the College, when hay and sheep and pasture were part of the budget. This close relationship of land and learning must have existed in all small rural American colleges, when both student and teacher lived much outdoors, and Hesiod and Virgil and Horace were not dusty poets but countrymen like themselves. A phrase I had read somewhere in my research echoed in my head: "a college must combine the refinement of Attic culture with the vigor of Spartan discipline"; and, I thought, as well the close acquaintance of man and land which was true in the ancient world, and which Jefferson valued so highly.

When the agriculture-poetry lesson was over I told Amos that I would not be able to come on Saturday because Tuckerman Butterweck was coming to stay with us. I was surprised to see his sudden smile. "Tell him to come and see me. I knew him well when he was in College."

"Was he one of your students?" Somehow I did not place Tucker in a Plato or Euripides class.

"No, I never could persuade him to take Greek. But he lived in this house for his first two years. After our little boy died it was so quiet here that I suggested to Rose that we take in a student who needed help. Tucker was a scholarship boy, and until he got the job of steward in the Gamma house he could not afford to live there. He tended our furnace and shoveled the walk and washed the windows. He even dug the garden for me one spring, but that was not so successful." Amos' mouth moved ruefully. "He dug up all my tiny Botanica tulips and threw them on the trash fire. When I reproached him — I came out just in time to see the last of them crackling — he said, 'You know, I thought they might be flowers!' Who would have thought he would grow up to make millions?"

I remembered then the conversation at the winter tea, and how Amos had said that if you believe in your luck as strongly as Tucker did, you have it. Something began to stir in my mind.

"Have you seen him often since college days?"

"Very seldom. He dropped in here once or twice when he was back — he was here last fall at Homecoming. But I have no real knowledge of him since he became a tycoon." Amos gave the little dry chuckling cough with which he always emphasized the daring use of what he considered some ultra-modern word. "It seems to me that I heard at the Faculty Club that he plans a gift to the College."

I told him about it. The whole campus was buzzing with all the real or imagined details, but Amos, living in eighth century Greece or this campus a hundred years ago, had not known of them.

"I do not think this is the best thing he could do with his money," he said when I had finished.

"Neither do we," I answered — the understatement of the year. "Perhaps," I went on, my idea taking firm grasp of me, "perhaps, when he comes to call on you this weekend, you might — you might say something about it?"

"If the subject arises," said Amos primly, "I might mention my views."

We turned to the study of the celebration held on the twenty-fifth anniversary of the founding of the College. President Champion had given "an elegant and inspiring address," according to the contemporary account, saying among other things (quite a few other things, I gathered, since it was reported that he talked for more than two hours):

> *We are low in funds in this institution, my friends, but this is no new situation. Our efforts are hampered, our Faculty underpaid, and our buildings in poor repair. Yet on all occasions when it seemed as though we had come to the end of our road, God's bounty was vouchsafed to us and we were allowed to continue in His work. We know that in these days also He will not forget us, and with the devoted aid of our friends He will continue to guide us and provide for us, so that our Institution may be in the years to come a beacon light in darkness and a tower of strength in the land.*

"Oh dear," I said, "don't show this to Mr. B., he will think it a prophecy in support of his building."

III

We worked hard over the weekend, but I did not think at the close that we had accomplished anything. Tucker was most pleasant, and so were we. But when it was over and he zoomed out of the drive in his Rolls we both felt as though we had spent forty-eight hours banging our heads against a stone wall.

We walked him about the campus, which was looking its worst. We did not have to worry about that, for he knew what March is like here and anyway he loved every mud puddle. All the time, cold, wet, eager, we talked about the need for a new library. And when this dropped unheeded, we talked about the need for a new arts building, a new biology-chemistry building, even a new gym; for it was clear that he wanted a big G. Tuckerman Butterweck Building. But none of our suggestions caused any positive reaction.

We wined and dined him elegantly all weekend, for he is fond of a good table and was most appreciative of my cooking. In fact over the *caneton à la bigarade* and the Clos Vougeot his round face grew so very flushed that I had a sudden horrible fear that he might drop dead before we got *any* gift. Through it all I found myself liking him in spite of his pig-headedness. He was nice with the children, though he is an old bachelor; he appreciated the dogs, and the way we have redecorated the old house, and he loved the horsehair mattress on the guest-room bed. But mules are compliant and granite tender compared with Tuckerman Butterweck. He must be intelligent, I thought, to be so successful; but that success has made him powerful and opinionated. I've read college novels about the wealthy and obstinate alumnus — we've got the prototype.

Although he listened to Mathias, his replies did not seem to have anything to do with the arguments and suggestions which the President made. Matt is not the most patient of men, and several times I saw the first edge of his temper. But he kept it under — you can do even that for three million dollars. As for Tuckerman, he was consistently calm and agreeable. I could not help but be impressed by his single-minded stubbornness under attack.

"You see, Tuck, we've always been an undergraduate, liberal arts college. That's our field, and that's where we do a first-class job. To superimpose a separate business school, with graduate work, on top of this doesn't make sense. Sometime, I hope, we can offer graduate work, when we have more endowment; but this should come little by little, and in the fields where we have already proved our excellence."

Poor Matt, I thought, he has said all this a hundred times before, he sounds like a phonograph record.

Tucker said, "My gift will enable you to bring in a number of new faculty, experts in the field of business, especially foreign trade — the cream, you might say, of business educators."

I could see Matt wince. "We're a small country college, Tuck, doing a good job, but a job that would be a lot better with a new library, or a higher faculty salary scale."

"The largest percentage of the alumni go into business — I looked up the figures. And what does the College do for them? Does it train them for the profession in which they will spend the rest of their lives? It must. And we can do as good a job as Columbia or Harvard."

And so on, all weekend. More than once I heard myself giving the placating nervous laugh which means I am afraid — afraid that somebody or something was going to explode on the spot.

I told Tucker about Amos and his eyes lighted. "Dear old Whitey, I certainly will go to see him. How good he was to me. And Mrs. Whitefield — what a lovely woman! I think I never married because I never could find any-one like her. Do you know she nursed me through the mumps? There wasn't much of an infirmary in those days and she kept me right there and looked after me, I was terribly sick too. That house was my real home while I was in college. I'll go down there right after lunch."

But when he came back from his call he was shaking his head. "Poor old Whitey, he's so lonely there. I guess he doesn't get much out of life any more."

"He gets a lot from seeing his old students," I said, "and I know that seeing you meant a great deal to him."

"How I respect that man! He seems to me the finest person I know — good all through, and what a brain. It makes me feel bad to see him so old and feeble."

Amos isn't really so old, I thought, he's not out of his seventies yet, and he's not a bit feeble; he could out-dig Tucker in the garden any day. But he must have looked slight and frail beside Tuck's heavy form. I was longing to ask, but dared not, if they talked about the Gift.

IV

The History fell into abeyance as the children, to celebrate the advent of spring, came down with a series of dreadful colds. In a fog of coughs, sneezes, vapor pots, aspirin, bed-trays and sleepless nights I lost two weeks of work for Amos.

We came also into one of those dark streaks of time when one bad thing happens after another. The dense un-starred nights, the days foggy with melting snow, the mud, the two feet of new snow after a day of hopeful sun and warmth — these were proper settings for tragedy. Not once but twice in March nights the calls came, one from the Dean, one from the State Police: and I knew with a dreadful constriction of the heart that far away, in a home in Connecticut or Ohio, a phone was ringing too, with the message that would end all the care and hopes and ambitions of a son's eighteen or twenty years. No amount of cruel repetition can ever accustom us to this: mad stupid reckless crazy students, you kill a piece of us when you kill yourselves.

And one morning I heard that little Mrs. Jaffe had gone to the hospital with a premature birth; and later, as I was getting the children's lunch, that the baby had been born dead. I pushed the peanut-butter and jelly sandwiches at them and went to find poor Ralph at the hospital. Not that there is much one can do, except provide a little compan-ionship; they were a lonely pair, and had not tried to make friends. After half an hour the head of his department came in and I walked home across the dingy snow, in a cold March wind that was riffling the willows which were just beginning to look yellow.

The youngest asked about it when he came home from school, and looked very sad when I told him. Our cat had just had kittens, a process which he attended for hours on end. "Perhaps she did not take the cellophane off quickly enough," he said.

•

But at last I could bring my mind to work again, and the day I went down the hill to Amos' I saw that the outline of the trees' twigs were blurred and the pussy willows were soft by the creek. When I arrived Amos took me to the window to see at the edge of the evergreens his first yellow crocus.

"I hear them," he said as though to himself, "they are beginning to speak in little voices of gold."

By now we had all the material for the History in good order, except for the very earliest period, when the valley was first settled and the College founded. The card-file, our legacy from Professor Satterwell, had been nourished with many additions, and contained almost all the references and quotations we needed; the books, pamphlets and catalogs were in perfect order by decades. But no writing had been done. Amos had made many beginnings on different chapters, but none were near finished. He was always being attracted to some new theme, to some happening in the story of the College that reminded him of a similar thing at another time — and there were dozens of these — which he had to look up, which led him to another parallel, until he became entangled in a maze of crossed lines, which of course demonstrated his thesis that the more different colleges we found the more we proved there was but one. Or again he would fall into a dream halfway through a sentence; some word would set him spinning tales with Odysseus in the swineherd's cottage, or discussing with Hesiod how to make a wagon, or merely remembering some day with Rose upon this campus long ago.

I wanted to urge him on; the College needed the History. But it was difficult to do. Indeed, he was influencing me more than I was influencing him.

That day we were studying Azel Champion, the first President of the College. He held that office for twenty-four years, so he spans its history from the very first days to the era of consolidation. He was a man six feet tall, the old description read, wiry and tough, with a harsh voice and a clear brow: "a man of the Doric order," strong, active, restless. He was not a great intellectual; his biographer explained kindly that he would have been more "renowned for mental exertion" in any one field had he not been forced by his position to attend to so many different interests. Indeed, he did everything in the little College:

taught, administered, raised money and raised buildings. He took his Theology class out to quarry stone for the second of the two halls which housed the institution and directed the masons who built it while he was sitting on the windowsill teaching a class in Greek.

Through all the heartbreaking vicissitudes suffered by his little band of students and teachers in this country, then still a raw poor frontier, he never lost heart, believing, as in the speech we had read the week before, that the Lord would provide and would not allow His devoted servants to fail in their endeavors. As we read and talked about him I saw the tall figure move across the hill, ready to fight or pray for his beloved College, casting a shadow far beyond his day.

There seemed, at least in retrospect, a wide simplicity about the lives and the efforts of those early founders. I do not suppose life seemed simple to them; it was too hard. But upon that frontier their aims were pure and their actions direct: to cultivate the wilderness, to walk justly before God and on cleared land, to build Him a church with the new-cut wood; to build a school so their children would know how to cast accounts, to vote, and to read the Bible; and to educate some of the young men so they could teach the Word of God. There was, of course, too, jealousy, narrowness, the seeking for power and money, and the bitternesses of failure. But I felt as I walked home across the campus which was once a farm, and before that a forest, and looked up to the chapel spire against the late light to the dark tuft beyond that was the head of the hemlock tree, close to their ambitions and their satisfactions, as though they walked beside me.

V

Spring was short-lived, the snow came back in the night, and blooming flowers and hopeful shoots were buried under a wet coverlet three inches thick. The birds were furious and I put out extra rations in their box. The only ones undeterred were the boys, who were out in the snow with baseball bats and gloves; it was, at least, easy to make spectacular slides to base.

Then Easter vacation came and more new snow on top of snowdrops and crocus. We sploshed wet-footed to a faculty party at the Club. Students are always prone to ask, "What do you all do when we're away?" And I always answer, "When we're rid of you we have a round of gay parties."

And it was moderately gay, though it was the time of year when there is a gray look about professors, and sometimes you wonder if they will have enough juice to last until June. Of course no one talked about anything but the Tower of Trade. As I listened I suddenly thought, perversely, that perhaps we were making — so to speak — a Tower out of a molehill. Of course the College would change, and have new buildings, not all of them beautiful.

Of course we needed a library more, but we would surely get it someday. Should we just give in to Tuck and agree?

As we had come up to the Faculty Club in the snow the high wide windows under the great Greek columns were uncurtained and brightly lighted and we could see the figures moving within; the sound of music came to meet us as the big double-leafed door opened, and I saw Amos with the light on his white hair. It was a perfect setting for him: grace and dignity within the grace and dignity of the handsome big old house. One of the best-known examples of Greek Revival in the state, it was built originally by Pharcellus Stutts, who had made a fortune in his tannery south of the town. He left it to the College, and for many years it was the President's House, and I wished it were still.

Amos was talking with, or rather listening to, young Rodd and Longridge of the English Department; they were discussing a change in the program for the senior year. "It's too easy," Longridge was saying. "In fact the senior year is just a breeze all the way. In fact the whole four-year program is perfectly childish in the demands it makes on the students. Look at the kind of world they're going to have to cope with — we must show them here how rough things are."

Rodd agreed. "We're getting superior students these days, we could get a lot more out of them. What do you think, Dr. Whitefield? Was the program easier in your day, or harder?"

Amos cleared his throat with a little ahem. "It was harder in that we had little choice of courses, and had to take the difficult ones whether we wanted to or not. And there were so many fewer students that the faculty could exert more individual pressure. It was not easy to get away with anything —" he smiled, "although I tried."

I moved on toward the table. There was a real stick in the punch and eyes were bright and talk high-pitched. I heard Mrs. Rodd, in a corner with Mannheim, giggling. Mrs. Stanislaus, drooping with boredom, was listening to Dr. Montgomery describe his latest acquisition of French porcelain. Little lame Dr. Sanderson, the son of the famous professor we were writing about in the History, was coming back to the table for another glass. It was all the same as the last party, the same as last year, the same as it had been for years and years.

My mind went back to the picture which Amos had drawn for me. He had first come to that house as a freshman at the turn of the century, anguished over his first pair of dress gloves. Theobald Stringer had been President then. "He had a close-cut white beard," said Amos, "and bleak blue eyes. When he stood in the parlor to greet you, in his frock coat and pearl-pinned tie, he looked like God — a jealous God, not to be trifled with. I had several courses with him — he taught philosophy, psychology, ethics and political science. They were all the same; Dr. Stringer was not interested in the subjects for themselves, but as tools to develop good moral character in us. He was about the last" mused Amos, "of the old-style professor; his only training had been in this College and in the Theological School. Scholarship and research in the modern sense were unknown to him. And in his teaching he made no attempt to bring interest into the subject; if it was difficult and monotonous for the student, so much the better for his moral character in mastering it!"

His wife had been a concert singer; her picture was before me, over the parlor mantel, all bosom in crimson brocade. She used to give recitals in this house, Amos said, that made the chandeliers rattle their prisms.

It was gayer when the Blessington Downers moved in. There was a bright fire on the hearth, coffee and cookies at hand, and a warm welcome in old God Bless' tremendous cordial tones for any student or professor who dropped in. Young Amos and his Rose were pets of the Downers, they were there often and to them the House was always the Downer house.

I said something of this to Amos as we drank punch together. Around us the voices buzzed and Amos' cheeks were flushed pink under the very blue eyes. "Sometimes, my dear, I feel that all the people I have known here in this house are still within it. I can see them in the crowd, I can hear their voices — even Mrs. Stringer's high C. They talk of the same things, they care for the same things, it is the community which it has always been."

"Yes," I said, "I suppose so." My eyes were on Rodd and Mrs. Mannheim, and from across the room I could hear

Dr. Stanislaus saying, "It will soon be over, I tell you, the day of the small liberal arts college is almost at an end. There is no place any more for this kind of little backwater school, everything will be in the big urban universities, in the laboratories of tomorrow."

VI

In April when the students came back from vacation the snow had disappeared for good and the first daffodils were showing along the Lilac Walk. Boys, like green shoots, seemed to be springing up all over the campus. As the dogs and I raced about checking to be sure each narcissus, each sea-blue scilla had reported for duty we seemed to be continually dodging baseballs, golf balls and convertibles. How long a year is at the age of nineteen or twenty, how amazing is the return of spring after the endless winter. Like bears coming out of their dens they moved about the campus as if wakened from a long sleep, and like giants refreshed tossed their heavy mackinaws on the wet ground to play ball, shouting through the softening air, feeling, like the creek, freedom from the weight of ice.

But in the midst of new life we had to go to a funeral, to see the just greening turf turned back on the hill, the newly unfrozen ground laid open and one more professor put away among the sleeping ones in the old old graveyard.

With the suddenness which makes each of us lay a hand

upon our hearts Dr. Montgomery was one day lively and active, the next day dead. We were talking with him Saturday at the faculty party, and today all who were at that party, and many more, were gathered under the drooping branches of the Norway spruce to hear the Chaplain say the last words over him.

He was always active, small, well set-up, his thick curly hair untouched by time except in color. It was only the year before that he gave up his daily run round the campus, trotting like a hackney pony, his white hair gleaming, his white knees gleaming below his running shorts. A bachelor, he was precise and prissy in his ways, so that it was hard to believe he was originally a boy from a bleak north-country farm. I do not know what started him out upon his academic career, but after graduating from the College he went to France to study, and at last came back to teach as a specialist in European history, with the emphasis on French. His students made fun of him because he lectured in outline: "There are five subjects to be considered in this period: A. the power of the clergy; subhead 1. the bishops; subhead 2. the local priests —" and so on.

In spite of this he was remarkably interesting and his course on nineteenth century France was a great favorite. He went to France almost every summer, and brought back favorite wines and cognacs and served them during the following year with delicious little *ragoûts* and *pot-au-feu* which he concocted himself in his perfectly furnished apartment.

He is gone away from among the copper pans and the bottles of *fine*, I thought, as I watched the coffin carried across the grass by students from his fraternity. What will become of the antique Quimper plates, the enamels, the Daumiers and the sketch by Corot? We will miss him, not only the gleaming figure running across the grass, but the teacher and exemplar of Gallic culture, who taught many a student not only the causes of the French Revolution but the provenance of claret and Burgundy and the fine distinctions among them.

We went away slowly down the hill, drawing the deep breath of reasserted life that always fills the lungs after a funeral. I stopped at the library to look up a date for Amos and met Paul Lightwood as I was going in. I had not seen him since that snowy evening when he had poured his restless thoughts into my ear.

"I see you're still here."

He grinned. "Yes. After I talked to you that night I went back to the dorm and wrote a long letter to my girl, and told it all over again. I think that two-times telling cured me. I've gotten very interested in my courses, especially this semester. Dad says he'll stake me to a trip with the Experiment this summer — that will give me some idea of what I want to do abroad."

"Good luck," I said, and as he went in I saw another boy standing by the door and stopped to talk. It was Tad Milbank, and we sat in the warming sun on the low wall of the old stone porch and talked about being a minister. I had known him well, for he was a scout master and our boys were fond of him. He was a gentle boy, with a full dark eye and a long upper lip like a Renaissance portrait; I could see him with a wisp of a mustache and a rose taffeta doublet slashed in gold. But that day he was rubbing his palms over his faded jeans and saying, "I *think* I want to be a minister, but I don't *know*. I've been lying awake nights thinking and thinking. I've talked to the Chaplain for hours, he must be sick of me by now. Is it the best way to do what I want in the world? Is the church really the place for me? Am I 'called'?"

Below the parapet the daffodils I planted six years ago were once more pushing up, sniffing the air to see if it was safe to rise and flower. "Life is so long," Tad was saying, "it is so hard to decide now for all those years to come. How can I know?"

How can I know? How many times had I heard that cry upon this campus? The daffodils know: they know the season and the hour, they survive the snow and ice because they know the sun returns. Six years or sixty and they will be here blooming, when college generations of Tads have faced their winters and their springs, decided and gone on.

"If you are not sure you had better not do it," I said abruptly. "Get a job, get out and around, don't go to graduate school or seminary now, go into the slums, into the hospitals, anywhere." I knew he came from a small midwestern city where his father was assistant superintendent of schools. And then I thought, agonizingly, it is easy to say "go," but how can *you* know?

The cold of the stone was penetrating; winter was still living in the wall, in the ground. In April, in July even the eternal cold is always near, always lying under the turf; but I did not want it to creep into me from that angle.

I got up. "Come and talk some more, Tad, as your ideas develop. And go see Dr. Hawthorn at the Congregational Church. He's had fifty years in the ministry, he can tell you — and he will tell you — the truth about it."

As I walked home with the *Agricultural History of New York State* under my arm, I thought about the alumni I meet whom I have known as students. What would Paul, what would Tad be like in ten years?

Some whom I have seen, whom I have known in college, are growing heavy, not only in body but in mind. A dull look creeps in around the eyes, the mouth loses its mobility, and a few moments' conversation shows that whatever spark was lighted here is dying or already dead. And as we see it we feel we are responsible.

What is done for the alumni of ten years hence depends upon what is done here today; decades after decades depend upon it. Faculty, curriculum, the students themselves — all of these must be handled with imagination and foresight and hard work — and money. None of it is easy, especially the foresight. The world of which our College is so small a part is moving very fast; Theobald Stringer had some confidence in the future, but we have none. Could it be true, I thought, kicking the gravel of our drive, could it be true what Stanislaus was shouting with such conviction? Is there no place for this College in the future? Will what it offers be of no value in the new currency of education? Does its history count for nothing, will there be no use for its tradition, for the ethos so long and so lovingly fostered?

VII

I could hardly persuade Amos into the study when the April days were fair. Each afternoon I found him in the garden, where now beneath the little grove of hawthorns at the far end the blue hyacinths and white were clustered, near the daffodils under the white birches. There were violets, and violas of every color. He picked me one. " 'There is pansies, that's for thoughts . . . there's a daisy . . .' " he smiled at the flowers. "It's his birthday today, I am tending the flowers in his honor. He must have learned his tenderness for flowers in the fields and woods along the Avon."

Reluctantly he brushed his knees and went to wash his hands. But his mind was still on the flowers, as we turned to our study of early days, "I do not think the first settlers brought much of a taste for flowers to this country; there was too much stress in their lives. But if they saw the hepaticas in the woods I hope they enjoyed them as much as I. Yesterday I went to the very top of the hill, and looked a long time for them without success. But at last I spied a little gathering of them, a tiny galaxy of white stars touched with rose and blue and set in silver fur. They seem to me symbols of new life, of the good life."

We turned to the early days, not of the College but of the village, which antedated it by a few decades. "There is a history of the village," said Amos, turning to the shelves. "It was begun perhaps seventy-five years ago but never finished. Part of it was published in the proceedings of the county historical society." He scrabbled about and finally pulled out a dog-eared pamphlet. "I found it in my father's papers in the attic when I moved away from the old home." He riffled the pages, then handed it to me. "See if there is anything we can use."

I read the first pages:

The Village lies in that part of the State which was opened to settlement at the close of the Revolutionary War. Previous to that time its only inhabitants had been the trappers and hunters of the earliest days, and an occasional settler whose small clearing and rough cabin was vacated during the bloody days of the War. As for the Indians, the district lies in the country of the Six Nations, and there is a legend that on this very site an Indian village existed at one time. The fields when opened by the plough yielded arrowheads, and Temperance Redfield when digging for a garden in the year 1821 discovered portions of several skeletons lodged in his property; there was a skull with an arrowhead embedded

*in it. An Indian trail, which followed the hills above the
river, was well used by the red men, and by the first of
the white men in this land. It is said also that on the hill
above the College, in a field now belonging to John Elwin
and cleared by his great-grandfather, Indian ceremonies
were conducted at certain seasons of the year, and that a
large stone in the northeast corner of the field played a
part in rites no less mysterious and bloody than those of
the ancients. The writer has examined the stone with
care, but time and weather have erased too well any
marks it may once have had.*

I skipped on, about the settlement by the New Englanders,
till I came to a name I knew from the annals of the College.

*In 1790 Isaac Garrow, of Southfield in Connecticut,
cleared land, built a cabin, and sent for his family, not
only his wife and infant child but his three brothers and
two cousins with their families. The fertility of the land
and the beauty of the scenery appealled to him so much
that he had no difficulty in persuading them to come, and
soon the nucleus of a small town appeared upon the
slopes above the Canowenda. They did not build upon
the banks of the stream itself at first; safety from Indians
and the position of the better land indicated higher sites.
But it was not long before a miller appeared to make use
of the excellent water-power. This was Job Leach, who
came from Massachusetts to build the first of several
mills along the stream. As the area filled up, the settlement, known as Leach's Mills, became the trading center,
a tavern was built and then a school. The name of the
first schoolmaster was Jared Topping and he was paid $8*

*a month. Wood to heat the building in the winter
months was donated by the parents, at the rate of half
a cord per child.*

The old chronicler rambled on, and I could see clearly
through his discursive pages the little settlement in the far-
reaching woods. We are inclined to think of the West
when we think of log cabins, Indians and the hardships of
the frontier; but they existed upon this soil beneath our
feet, by this river, beneath this very tree. And the names in
the chronicle were the names of the founders of the College. Isaac Garrow was its first benefactor, upon his farm
it stands. And Jared Topping graduated from school-
teaching to the Hill, and taught Natural Philosophy until
he was an old old man. I shut the little book and handed it
back to Amos. "It is all part of the same, college and town
and countryside, it is all one."

~ V

When I heard that the trustees had voted to accept the Butterweck gift, in the original form in which it was offered, I was so disappointed and upset that I flew off to Amos for consolation. It was a brilliant bitter-cold morning, even though it was the first of May. In front of the house my little Scarlet Emperors had laid their heads right down upon the ground. But above them in the cornel bushes a flock of cedar waxwings, their well-tailored glossy suits glinting with red and yellow, moved from berry to berry, hissing softly in the sunlight.

Amos looked tired, I thought, and I had some remorse at putting my troubles before him. But, after all, they were his troubles too, and all of ours who loved the College. I talked for a long time about Tucker and his Tower, about our position, the trustees' position, and most of all Tuck's position and our inability to budge it. I knew that he was coming to the campus the following week, and I was hoping that Amos would have a go at him; but I could hardly tell him to.

Amos listened without comment, his close-cut gleaming head on one side, his expression attentive and questioning, as though I were a candidate for a degree defending a thesis. And he was as noncommittal as an examining professor when I had finished. "I see. I see. Yes, I understand the point of view."

I did not press him, and indeed at that moment Connard Leach arrived with a bag of fertilizer for the garden. After a brief but snappy rundown of the day's political news, we fell to talking of our current phase of the history, the early days of town and gown.

"My great-great-great-grandfather came here from Massachusetts by way of Vermont," Connard said, "but not all in one journey. He liked best to build new dams, new mills, and he came step by step in twenty years, leaving behind him a trail of monuments — sawmills and gristmills below their new ponds. I took a trip once when I was younger and looked up the way he had come; many of the mills are still there, and the ponds too. I thought it was like a giant whose footsteps behind him filled with water. I think he loved running streams as some men love running horses, and when he got to the Canowenda, he liked her as well as any he had ever seen, and never left her."

"Maybe your great-great-great-grandmother was tired of moving," I said.

Connard had a sharp harsh cackle like a crow laughing. "I'm sure she was. I've heard tell she was very nervous about the kids and the water, and insisted that each one should learn to swim as soon as it could walk or before. They must have been a great crew, splashing about in the millponds; there were thirteen — kids I mean — and they must have been tough, for everyone lived to grow up — that's why there's so many Leaches in these hills. Well, Job Leach sawed the planks for the first school — there were forty-eight children in it and Jared Topping was the schoolmaster."

"I know about him," I said, "he taught in the College later."

"Job Leach was a pretty old man by the time the College was founded," said Connard, "but he donated a lot of lumber for the first building — the one that stood where the chapel is now. That was the center of the land Isaac Garrow gave for the institution but it turned out to be awful muddy, there was a spring just above. Later they put in some pipe and turned it into another course."

"I know," I said again, for the bright water runs today out of the hillside below the chapel, sparkling and talking down to the little lake, a veritable spring of Parnassus, an undercurrent of music for all the teaching done beside its waters. But Amos was muttering to himself, "O fons Bandusiae splendidior vitro."

"Isaac Garrow must have been quite a fellow," I said.

"He was a man of great vision," said Amos sententiously. "He was not an educated man himself, but he wanted education in this valley. He was the first to organize the building of the school and the first to dream of a College."

"And they had religion," added Connard, "especially his wife — she was a powerful religious woman. I know, her sister married my great-great-grandfather and there's been a powerful strain of religion in the family ever since." He grinned at Amos. "I'll carry the fertilizer into the garden if you'll tell me where you want it put."

I did not stay, for Amos admitted he had not slept much the night before and planned to nap — both the admission and the nap were unusual for him. But to tell the truth we had not slept much ourselves, for it was the first night of Spring Party, and music, yelling and screeching of cars had lasted well into the morning. We are always torn, Matt and I, between sympathy for the young having fun, fear about the cars, and just middle-aged annoyance at broken sleep.

The next night we went to the dance in the gym, and I fell into the usual softened mood. As they moved about the floor in the patterns of the music through the dimness under the high roof, they seemed to move from girls and boys to women and men, the social persons within growing and stretching to fill the already mature bodies. The awakenings and growths of the mind we work with here day by day; this is our business. But on weekends like this we see the development of the other side, as fascinating as the slow-motion movies of the growth of a plant. Hands, eyes, voices, laughs, every expression of the body betrays the stage and rate of maturity, and each symptom can be appealing or frightening. And always, in such a group, there are breathtaking moments of beauty, some girl transfigured by happiness or passion, so that we see Juliet dancing: "Earth-treading stars that make dark heaven light." Or a boy, some feckless uncouth boy that I know well in plainer moments, looking suddenly like a young Lancelot, a Galahad, or the son of Peleus himself. We know only too well that their hearts are not pure; but for all their silly ways we feel their strength, we have confidence in their future.

Watching the dance, deafened by the music, I saw the figures flow from year to year: that is not Tad I see, but Jim who graduated five years ago; over there is Rick, who was killed in the Philippines; and there Conrad, who helped us move in our furniture the day we arrived on campus and was lost the following summer on the German front. For all the changes in dances, in music, in dress and manner, a ball is still the same, and there move behind this frieze of short skirts and white dinner jackets figures with draperies whirling in the waltz, the patterns of Lancers forming, and an echo of a Schottische where gleam white ties and white gloves. I see Amos and his Rose, and Blessington Downer dancing the polka. There were times of course when there was no dancing on this campus, but still over the years sound the dancing feet.

II

As exam time drew near I could not get into the library to do any research. I only pushed in to get the book on Jared

Topping and early higher education in New York State. The poor old building was bursting at the seams as the students crowded in to finish the papers due last week, to catch up on the studying for exams they should have started a month ago. I climbed over outstretched feet in dirty shoes, pushed aside lounging bodies, kicked aside jackets hung up on the floor, and did not attempt to stay long in the atmosphere of studying boy. I wish old Butterweck, I thought savagely, had to write a term paper in here, stand in line for his books, and find no table or desk to sit at, no good light and no fresh air.

Actually I had given up trying to do any more research for the History; we had about all the material we could use, unless we expected to write a history of education in New York State. It was hard enough, I thought, to get Amos to cope with the essentials of the history of *this* College; he was so enamoured with every detail that I could not see how he was ever going to sort, select and put down on paper the heart of the story. I could see that next year would be a real battle to get the manuscript done on time. But I was ready for it, for I knew he could do it — in his own good time.

As I took the book down to Amos', I checked over the campus trees. Influenced by the approach of exam time, I marked their progress. The maples were in the lead, they rated A's, for their forked flat leaves were fully out; if there is any shape more perfect than a hard maple leaf I do not know it, and year after year they give us perfect ones. The elms were close behind, though their leaves were tiny; the great wine-glass elm was not leafed at all — is it because the sap has so far to go from root to crown? The basswoods were laggard, and as for the locusts, they were at the foot of the class; like some students they might have been dead for all the life they showed. But like the students each has his own timetable, and what lagged now would be all the fairer later, when feathery leaves and sweet drooping white blossoms would make them the most beautiful of all.

Amos of course was in the garden; the tulip buds were beginning to color, and he could not wait for his Spirits of the Night to bloom. The daffodils were in full splendor, the sun was warm on our backs and we could not bear to go in and stood among the flowers talking of Tucker's visit.

"I don't think he believes in libraries," I said ruefully, "he told me that when he was in college he never went into the library at all. The professors gave out textbooks, you learned the textbook backward and forward and that was that."

"Greatly exaggerated," said Amos.

"But I think he regards reading in a library as a peripheral activity, not really necessary to education — something you do with your feet up when it's raining."

"I know that he believes that students should be out and around — in his words," said Amos. "He told me so himself. He said he thought they should Learn from Life." The caps were easily discernible in Amos' voice.

"Tell him how hopeless the old library is," I said. "Tell him there isn't room for the students to get in, tell him the books are piled up in the sub-sub-basement next to the furnace. Tell him it's like a stack of sardine cans full of sardines. Tell him —"

Amos shook his head and made a little negative movement with his hands. "I can only tell him what I truly believe is best for this campus, what will support its great traditions and build new ones." He spoke formally, then coughed a little. "I may say this does not seem to me to include a Gothic Tower."

Like a king Amos could indicate when a conversation upon a certain topic was over. We went inside and turned to Jared Topping.

"He was the first real intellectual, if I may use so imprecise a term, to be associated with the young College," said Amos, his fingers in the church-steeple position. "As a very young man he came here as the first schoolmaster to the little village, but later taught in the College for many decades. He had attended Dartmouth, but after that he educated himself, by books and by men. In fact — "he riffled the pages of the little book I had brought — "he was much criticized in the new little settlement — here —" he read aloud, " 'For all his success as a teacher in the little school of raw wood, with the windows of real glass brought all the way from Albany, Topping was considered to be dangerously over-educated. His room in Isaac Garrow's house, where he boarded, was full and running over with books. "I do not think he is a godly young man,"

wrote Hannah Garrow in her diary, "he reads pagan au-
thors in Latin and Greek. What need has anyone of more
than the one Book?" ' "

We laughed together, at the narrowness of the small
community, its hostility to ideas — but then I thought,
What are we laughing at?

III

By the third week in May exams were in full swing; a
great hush settled over the campus. Not even on Saturday
night was there any cacophonous singing and beer-can
throwing. The profs were busy reaping their harvests,
hoping for a rich yield from the thin little blue books full
of almost illegible writing. There was an air of endings
over everything; faculty and students alike were looking
forward to travel, to summer jobs, or to summer school on
the campus. Only the administration, it seemed, must remain in the rut; there are always new plans to be made,
new students to process (as they say in the office), and
always new money to raise.

Money! Tucker had come and gone, but the situation
was unchanged. He did spend a long afternoon with
Amos, on a miserable day — for we always seemed to
have bad weather when Tucker came, as though the sky
reflected our worry. The rain pelted down, knocking the
tulips about and puddling the grass. But I am sure that

Amos took him into his study, got out the bottle of "Early Times" he kept in the chimney cupboard, and turned upon him all the slow-burning, powerful effect of his quiet, hesitant, persistent personality. I did not see Tucker afterward, but Matt said he was very thoughtful and quiet as they went to dinner with the faculty committee.

I was brooding over all this in chapel the next morning, while I was looking at the students. There were not many there that last Sunday; some had finished their exams and gone home, some were studying hard for the coming week — when, of course, they should have been in chapel praying for help. There were so few I could almost consider them individually, wondering as I studied them what kind of college is best. That dreaming one under the window with the elf-locks over his forehead and down his neck — liberal arts were right for him. But perhaps Pete Sinclair, just beyond, would be better off in a course on management than one on epic poetry. But when would he read Dante or *Paradise Lost* or Gibbon or Aristotle if he did not read them now? And are we to let him go through life without ever drinking delight of battle with his peers far on the ringing plains of windy Troy? What do we owe him: a skill, or a thought? Or both? Or only the ability to find either for himself?

As we stood on the steps outside, in the moist air of spring, chatting with students and faculty — An inspiring talk, Dr. Greene; The choir sang exceptionally well this morning, Jon; When do you leave, Mrs. Bronson?; How is

your mother, Bill? — Arne Olafsson came eagerly to us,
"I've got the Fellowship to London University, sir. It's all
set for next year." His sky-blue eyes were dancing, his
ears pink with excitement; and our congratulations were
deep and warm. He had been hoping for this all year, for
his sake and for the College's; it was the first time a student from here had won this highly competitive award.
But I wondered, as we went down the steps, what this boy
from Minnesota would make of London, he who has never
been east of the Hudson in his whole life. Surely he would
miss the great skies above his native farm, and the easy
ways of our campus. But I could see he had no doubts or
hesitations; the world had opened its door and the view
was wonderful.

As we walked down the hill the sun came out; the rain
had pushed spring forward, already we were headlong for
summer. The grass, the lilacs as we walked under the old
tall bushes, the very leaves of the trees smelled sweet. And
for those brief moments our work too smelled sweet and
rewarding, and we thought that perhaps after all our College is best.

We had a few faculty people in for cocktails that evening, and sat or stood on the terrace in the spring dusk, de-
lighting in the cool green around us and the cool drinks in
our hands. Red Birnbaum was asking me about the history and our approach to it, and under the influence of a
few sips of martini I was trying to tell him something of
our feeling about the continuity of the College throughout

its history, the integrity of tradition and locale, in short, the Immortal Person.

He listened quizzically, twirling his glass and watching the orioles in the wine-glass elm. I must have described our purpose badly, for he laughed suddenly, turning upon me the sharp glance of his slanted eyes. "You are mystics, you and Amos Whitefield, fuzzy mystics who sentimentalize the College and its people. You see it all in a kind of glamour, a kind of pseudo-intellectual sanctity that belongs to the tradition of the fifty-year class."

He had had two and a half martinis or he would not have spoken out like this to me, frank as he is, good friends as we are. I looked from the terrace across the sloping lawns to the flash of the chapel spire like a golden fruit in the new-leafed elms.

"Maybe," I said, "but there is something here we feel, we *all* feel, including you, and that we are trying to analyze and describe. How else can you account for what people feel about colleges and universities?"

He laughed. "They feel plenty of things."

"Don't cloud the question."

"No, I understand what you think you mean. But aren't you being a little Berkeleyan, saying that because men are sentimental about colleges, and believe in them, as in a goddess, there must be a shrine of some real divinity on the campus?"

"Don't you think there is?" I said.

"I didn't find it at Chicago."

"I'm not talking about Chicago, as you know very well. I'm talking about a small piece of ground on a hilltop above a river, where among trees and springs men have prayed and built and taught and learned for a century and a half, and are still doing it, and will do it tomorrow and still a century and a half hence, God willing."

I found I was getting a little warm myself, though my first drink was not half gone. The sound of the bell came to us through the trees and I moved into the house to gather up my guests.

"Wait till you read our History," I tossed back at him as he grinned at me out of his fox eyes, "you'll be converted to our religion and will believe in our goddess."

I was thinking it over in bed that night as I heard the owl call from the pines. I remembered how in the fall, that day when the leaves were turning golden, I had first thought of the College as an Immortal Person: the entity which, among the fading creations of men, survived over the centuries, multiple in form, single in purpose, firmed by tradition and continuously inspired — in a literal sense — by some kind of faith, of hope. Throughout the year, as I studied its history, I saw how, successively incarnated, it preserved similar contours and kept under top hat and whiskers or cap and crew cut a uniformity of feature. And it seemed to me, as I had watched Amos, on the Hill, in the garden, at his desk, that here again was such a Person, passing for a few decades through this slight container, and looking out upon its demesne and current history through the sea-blue eyes that were so often raised to mine across the piles of records of the past.

IV

Decoration Day was fair, though cold, and the bright flags blew out bravely. I watched the parade, as usual, with tears in my eyes; the children marched past, my own among them in the school band or the scouts. I had spent the previous evening pressing uniforms and sewing on badges; and then I could hardly admire my handiwork for the tears.

In the cemetery the grass was damp, and we shifted our feet as we stood listening to a really stunning series of platitudes. The legionnaires fired an awkward salute, and the cows in the next field skipped away startled. The notes of Taps shivered softly through the maple leaves. And we straggled away homeward in the sunshine, smiling foolishly at each other, the possessors of a secret renewed and reaffirmed.

In the afternoon, when the boys were all out playing ball, I went to Amos' — and received the surprise of my life. He handed me a folder of manuscript. "Now you can start typing the History," he said with his little crooked smile; he liked fooling me, he liked my surprise. I looked at the pages of yellow legal paper. His writing was very small and crooked like his smile, but it was legible and as beautiful as a medieval manuscript.

"But this is the beginning," I said stupidly.

"Yes. We have done our research and study from the top down — like Schliemann at Troy, as I told you. Thus, having seen results, we recognize causes, and in the seeds know what plant will bloom. Now I plan to do the writing from the bottom up, so to speak. This is the first chapter."

I dropped into the old black leather chair to read.

THIS VERY TREE

1

The hemlock tree stood a little below the hill, in a level space which formed a terrace between the upper and lower slopes above the Canowenda. In a country of notable trees this hemlock was already one of the finest; it was a trailmarker for the Indians as they passed from ridge to ridge through the original forest.

Under this tree had stood no white men until now. This valley and its hills had been passed by when the eager feet of empire-seekers pushed along the Hudson, the Mohawk and the Susquehanna. Those who stood under it now were not passers-by; they were farmers from Connecticut, seeking good land, stone-free land, on which to settle. And here they found it.

I looked up to smile at Amos; I had not known we had this tree in common. But he had slipped away to the gar-

den, and I could see him through the window, digging this
very soil. I turned the pages before me.

The first family to settle here was that of Isaac Garrow,
who cleared the land on the slopes and levels around the hemlock tree. As a boy he had wished to be a minister, and at
Litchfield in Connecticut he had had more schooling than most
farm boys. But he was not cut out to be a scholar, nor did
he feel, in the end, that he was called to preach the Word of
God. Yet he maintained throughout his life a great devotion
to learning and a respect for education. It was he, when the
small settlement grew large enough to provide a quiverful of
children, who organized and built the first school.

I glanced down the page, lost in the America of long
ago.

Into the wild country of New York people were coming, by
the dozens and then by the hundreds. Far beyond the Alle-
ghenies the campfires moved westward night by night, but
along the Canowenda part of that tide stopped their wagons
and unhitched their oxen. The Indian trail was marked now
with wheel-ruts, and the sound of falling trees and the smoke
of their burning spread through the land. Strange faces became neighbors, and on these hills grew the shape of a community, even the semblance of a town.

Leach's Mills was its first name —

I skipped over toward the end of the chapter.

But Isaac Garrow was not satisfied, after some years, with the thriving school and the excellent schoolmaster from Massachusetts, Jared Topping. Nothing would do but that they must have an institution of higher learning, an Academy. He talked to his neighbors about it, but found little enthusiasm. The stumps were still in the hillsides and it was hard enough to get a living. It was not until ten years later that he received the support he needed for his dream.

During the first years of the settlement religious services had been held in the log cabins and rough frame houses where they lived. A congregation was organized, and one or another of the citizens conducted the services, Isaac Garrow among them. But after ten years they were able to build a church, on the first level above the river, not far from the mill and the tavern. And then they sent back to Litchfield for a minister. With his coming, in the spring of the first year of the nineteenth century, began a new era for the little town.

I called to Amos through the window. "It's good. Keep on writing, and I will type this and bring it back tomorrow." He smiled at me but did not answer. He was out of breath from digging; and could it have been also from excitement to know what I thought of our at-last first chapter?

·

When I went home I found Butch Blochmann who had come to say goodby. He had had his last exam and was off to spend the summer back on the farm. "I could get good pay working somewhere else," he said, "but Dad counts on my coming back to help him."

Butch had grown up during the year; once again I saw that the timid worried freshman had turned into a casual competent almost-sophomore. Butch had had further to go than most; but, I thought, the magic is working.

"It's been a good year," he said, "thank you for all you've done for me."

I hadn't of course done anything for him; he had done it for himself, as well as a great deal of window-washing and snow-shoveling and boy-sitting for me.

"Have a good summer, Butch, we'll be glad to see you back in the fall." And it was true: I see them go, speeding down the hill in convertibles, or like Butch waiting at the bus-stop with two suitcases, a laundry box, a tennis racket and a guitar; I see them go with no regret, we have been together long enough, it is time to part for greener pastures. But before September comes I am eager to greet them, to see them back bigger, browner, more grown up than ever. Have a good summer, Butch.

v

I met Amos downtown, as I was going to market to lay in the first stocks of supplies for the Commencement season. We stopped to talk, and almost with one accord we walked together to stand on the bridge over the Canowenda, at the foot of Main Street. The river really belongs to the town rather than the College; it was of course the cause of the town, with the power burning in its white falls above the rocky ledges. But the College too has made it its own; the upper reaches far above the dam are peaceful for canoes and swimmers, there are fish for anglers and birds for watchers. And sometimes in the silent nights, when the dark surface moves like molten glass, it has tempted to a final solution some unhappy student.

Amos and I felt its power as we stood leaning on the rail, mesmerized by the moving water, hearing — between the cars and trucks — the sound of its gnawing at the banks, at the abutments of the old bridge.

"Canowenda," said Amos, "Canowenda." He turned to me. "Did you know that Coleridge and Leigh Hunt wanted to settle on the banks of the Susquehanna just because of its beautiful name?"

We went back to his house together after the marketing — mine so large, his so small, for he seemed to eat almost nothing. He had a new folder of ms. for me in the painstaking script; at once I was engrossed in it.

2

The man sent from Connecticut to be the minister of the new church on the banks of the Canowenda was Azel Champion. He was destined to be not only the leader of the congregation

but of the whole community, and, with Isaac Garrow, the
founder of the College itself. We do not know very much
about his life before he came west into New York State, except
that he was born near Stanbridge and went to school there, and
afterwards to Dartmouth College, where he eked out a living
by teaching school for part of the year. He was thirty-one
when he came here, and had had but one church before this
one.

Many years later Isaac Garrow was to tell of the day that
Azel Champion came to the valley. "It was spring," he said
to his interviewer, on his ninetieth birthday, "and I was plowing the upper field, where the College stands now. The leaves
were just breaking out on the maples, they was the size of a
squirrel's ear. It was warm for the season, and I stopped to
rest myself and my oxen in the shade of the big hemlock on the
slope. I would never let anyone cut that tree, all the years I
worked clearing land on the hill. And it still stands there, only
a little bigger than when I first come into this country, in
seventeen ninety.

"I remember that day I looked down over our valley, and
thought how quick the town had grown — we had two mills
by then, and the tavern and the store, and of course the school.
And I could just see among the trees the new wood of the
church a-shining. I was just going back to my plowing when
I see somebody coming up the hill. He come up with a long
stride, like he had come a long way and wasn't tired. He was
a tall feller, taller than me, and his big hands hung down half-
curled like he knew what it was to work. He was young, I
could see, but he looked — well — weathered, like a tree.
And I liked him that first minute I saw him.

"He told me he was the new minister, sent from Litchfield,
and I told him I was the senior deacon, and we knelt down to

pray, under the tree. And he prayed as though he was talking direct, and he told what we wanted and needed in this valley, like good harvests and freedom from sickness and savages, and a strong congregation and a fine church. I knew right away that he was a man with vision, and a man of action too. And his prayer was heard; for all these things came to pass, and more too that we did not speak of that day under the hemlock tree."

I had read this account of the interview with Garrow in a pamphlet which we owed to the burrowings of Satterwell; and now I could see even more clearly the figures of the two powerful and rugged young men under the tree, around them the still-new land, the still oxen, below on the hillside the buildings of the small settlement above the gleaming Canowenda.

I read on.

Azel Champion had not been long resident in the valley when Isaac Garrow told him of his dream for an Academy, and found in the new minister an enthusiasm that matched his own. It was some years before they gathered to them the necessary support in men and money. But in 1809, the year that Abraham Lincoln was born, a meeting in Garrow's house determined the founding, first of the Academy, and eventually of the College.

The village was by that time sufficiently well-grown to be concerned, and able to provide some money and materials for the first building. This was constructed, needless to say, by the hands of the founders themselves. Champion was a notable stonemason, and the two-story building which housed the first students and teachers, their classes and religious services, stands today upon the campus as foursquare as when Azel set the stones. And the land itself was given by Isaac Garrow, the whole of his upper farm.

I went on to the account of the ceremony held at the dedication of the building a year later; this I had found myself, in a family history published in the 'eighties in Ohio. But before I could finish Amos called me from the garden.

He was sitting on the great stone, as I had sat on the first day I came to him to talk about the History. The leaves were turning then, as these new brilliant ones in green would turn in their own time. I dropped to the grass, beside the Spirits of the Night. There, with Amos among the scent of the late lilacs, I felt like a soft wind the passage of time. We are in our citadel, I thought, defending ourselves against the enemy by partaking of this process of education, which, like birth, hurts both the giver and the receiver while it is going on, but which like birth brings life and opportunity. We think we are immortal because we are continually among a crowd, continuously renewed, of young people. The student is young forever, and his older colleagues dream that so are they. And beside me was the embodiment of this youth of the spirit, drawing his strength not only from the ethos of the College but from the America of an earlier day, of the Jeffersonian tradition, illuminated and explained by the democracy and poetry of a classical antiquity.

Through the sun-warmed grass came the intimation of earth's lasting cold. The nest-building orioles in the elm, whom he had called me to see, flashed gold in the feathery foliage. Amos looked to me suddenly immeasurably old, a white-headed seer from a long-dead past; but the eyes that followed the birds were as bright as the sky.

VI

With a houseful of trustees and honorary degree candidates I had no time to go to Amos'. Tuckerman Butterweck was staying with us, a half-smile on his round face; the gift of the Tower of Trade was to be announced at Commencement. He told me he had spent the evening before with Amos. They had sat in the garden in the dusk, by the white peony bush. He did not say what they talked about.

I moved about the house that day in a daze of disappointment and sick regret. The night before Matt had said, as we were getting ready to go to bed after a long long day, "I just can't stay here. I would not be able to develop the School of Business with any honest conviction; I can't live with the Tower of Trade. It's not fair to the College and the trustees to pretend that I can. They'll have to get somebody else." He pulled off his tie with a yank. "I've made up my mind. I'm just not sure whether to announce it now or later."

I was appalled. "Now?" I said feebly. The idea of course was not new to me; I had realized that this might happen, as Matt became more and more unhappy. But I had turned away from a thought which I could not bear. To leave? To leave this hill, this College? And to do it *now?* This knife would cut too deep. . . .

"Oh no," he said, lying down in the bed as though he never meant to get up, "oh no, I suppose I can't do it now. But I will."

But there was no time next day to brood or weep. I went to the chapel to go over the seating of distinguished guests with the head usher. The brass chandeliers had been polished to gold, the windows gleamed, the fingermarks were gone from the white walls. I thought of the rows of boys in caps and gowns, the parents behind watching, stuffed with pride.

And in the evening, as soon as it began to be dark, we went down the hill to the little lake for the torchlight ceremony. We stood in silence along the banks as the seniors in cap and gown marched by with flaring torches, lined up on the opposite bank and sang the Alma Mater. The music came sweet and faltering across the water, sad and final; a mood broken abruptly when at the end they hurled the torches into the water with warwhoops worthy of the earlier inhabitants of these hills. All the College people like the Torchlight; fire, song and water we never grow tired of, each year we watch with joyful melancholy.

I looked for Amos there, and was surprised not to see

him; he loved Torchlight too and had seen it fifty times. I
noticed, as I drove our guests back to the house, that there
was no light in his study. Either he was out for supper
and the evening — a most unusual proceeding — or he
was sitting too long in the garden in the damp, admiring
the white peonies . . .

When I had settled everyone in my house with drinks,
and a lively discussion on the relative merits of single ver-
sus co-education, I slipped out and drove down to Amos'
house.

The front door was open, as though someone had just
passed through. I stepped inside and called, but only the
deliberate tick of the grandfather clock in the hall answered me. I went into the study and turned on the lamp
by the desk.

He was there, in his easy chair, and I thought he was
asleep. I had seen him dozing there before, his head leaning back against the old leather, his hands relaxed, his
eyes closed. But now his eyes were open, looking toward
the window, as though he saw the Hill and the College. It
was a peaceful look, there had been no convulsion and I
think no pain.

I knelt beside the chair, my hand upon his, already
cold. On the desk were the pages of the fine writing for
Chapter III. I read the first sentence:

It may be that Isaac Garrow and Azel Champion and the
other stalwarts, who founded and built with their own hands

the Academy which was the precursor of our College, did not foresee as they set the stones with faith and courage how long both stones and faith would last. But it may well be that they did, in their devout belief in "morality and education," and would be pleased but not surprised to see what it has become today.

Be that as it may . . .

When I had told Matt, and the trustees, and they had taken over, I went to find Tucker and told him, and we sat and talked of Amos and all that he had meant to the College. Tucker was not a man to speak of his feelings, but I saw in the worn phrases he fumbled with how much he was moved. When at last, weary with shock and sorrow, I went to bed, he was still sitting in our library, our books about him, an untasted glass before him.

•

But a college is, must be, as Amos said so often, immortal. Commencement unrolled its course as usual. After breakfast came the usual scurry for caps and gowns, Matt in his usual indecision as to which of his many hoods to wear. I, in spite of the ache in my breast, was worrying about the luncheon, the children, and all the ordinary affairs with which we wind up the college year. I got my lady guests marshaled after the men had gone up the hill; fluttering with summer chiffon and streamered hats we ambled after.

The chapel was full of more chiffon and hats; mothers seem to feel it necessary to wear to the graduation of their sons the same kind of ensemble they wear to the weddings of their daughters. It looked as gay as a garden, a fair background for the academic procession in black robes touched with bright color. But the faces of the faculty were sad, or so it seemed to me; and the music was grave and slow. Our organist had been a good friend of Amos, and the low notes sang like a requiem.

I did not hear much of the Commencement Address. The distinguished visiting fireman had eaten a good breakfast at my table, and he put all his strength into it. It was, I heard dimly, better than the usual run. But I was in the garden, among the tulips, watching Amos dig the soil he loved so well, his head in the sun shining as white as the Siberian iris, as the birches at the end of the lawn.

But I listened carefully, as always, to the conferring of degrees. This is a moment which never loses its excitement, as each class comes up for the final accolade, to the point where they are marked, not Finished, but Ready to Begin. From my seat at the side I looked down the rows of faces under the caps with the tassels shifted to the other side. They looked, for once, serious and impressed; some, to be sure, looked haggard, for there had been a good deal of noise around the campus in the night. But here and there I snatched a glimpse of purpose, faith, will — call it what you wish. Behind them the parents hung over the ceremony, the mothers wiping their eyes, the fathers staring straight with pride, the little brothers and sisters ceasing from wiggling for this one moment.

Then the last senior-now-alumnus was back in place; you could see them breathe out a long sigh of gratification and relief. The applause rolled and echoed for minutes and minutes. Then everyone settled themselves and the choir rose for the triumphal chorus which they sing every Commencement.

On the platform I could see Tucker in the second seat beyond Matt, with the Chaplain in between. As I watched I saw him write something on his program and pass it over to Matt. An unreadable expression crossed my husband's face, and he leaned across the Chaplain's ample front to whisper urgently to Tucker. Tuck nodded firmly. What could it mean? Some new twist to torture us about the Tower of Trade? If my heart had not already been as low as it could get, it would have sunk.

The music ceased, Matt rose to award the honorary degrees, which he did with his usual grace and aplomb. Again applause rang through the chapel, this time merely polite. Matt, at the rostrum, waited for silence.

"I have a special and important announcement to make at this time." I wanted to stop my ears; my hands had made my program damp and curling. "As many of you know, our distinguished alumnus, Mr. G. Tuckerman Butterweck of the Class of '17, is this year making to the College the largest gift which it has ever received. Mr. Butterweck had just informed me that it is his wish, if the trustees approve, that the gift should be used to build a new library, to be called the Amos Whitefield Library, in honor and in memory of his and our beloved friend and teacher who left us yesterday."

I was too stunned to clap. But around me the clapping and cheering was like the roar of waves; I was in a sea of it. Everyone, faculty, students, families, trustees was applauding with all his might, everyone wore the kind of smile which I could see, dimly, on Matt's face. Dimly, for the tears came fast, the tears I had not shed when I found him, and I made no attempt to dry them.

·

As we came out from the chapel the blossoms from the tall old locust trees were drifting down in the soft air like sparse sweet-scented snow. The pigeons clapped their wings as they flew up to the roof of Azel Champion's first building. Beyond the Chapel I looked up to the site of the new library, and beyond it on the hillside to the hemlock tree.